Assessment Sourcebook

THE UNIVERSITY OF CHICAGO SCHOOL MATHEMATICS PROJECT

TRANSITION MATHEMATICS

INTEGRATED MATHEMATICS

About Assessment
Assessment Forms
Chapter Quizzes
Chapter Tests, Forms A, B, C, and D
Chapter Tests, Cumulative Forms
Comprehensive Tests
Answers
Evaluation Guides

Scott Foresman
Addison Wesley

Editorial Offices: Glenview, Illinois • Menlo Park, California
Sales Offices: Reading, Massachusetts • Atlanta, Georgia • Glenview, Illinois
Carrollton, Texas • Menlo Park, California

http://www.sf.aw.com

Contents

ISBN: 0-673-45752-4

Copyright
Scott, Foresman and Company, Glenview, Illinois
All Rights Reserved.
Printed in the United States of America.

7 8 9 10 11 12 – DBH – 04 03 02 01

Pages	Contents

Tests

Answers
Quizzes; Tests, Forms A and B, Cumulative Forms; Comprehensive Tests

Evaluation Guides
Tests, Forms C and D

Assessing Student Performance in Mathematics

The Changing Face of Mathematics Instruction and Assessment

In the past decade, the National Council of Teachers of Mathematics and other mathematics education organizations and professionals have examined the methods teachers use to instruct students in mathematics and have recommended ways to improve this instruction. Their recommendations stress the importance of providing more diverse methods of instruction including activities, open-ended investigations, and long-term projects, many of which utilize cooperative learning. They challenge us to make the goal of mathematics the acquisition of the dynamic processes of critical thinking and problem solving, rather than merely the mastery of a static body of facts and procedures.

Instruction and assessment are closely linked. As instructional methods change, the methods of evaluation need to change. New forms of assessment being proposed provide a more authentic way of evaluating the depth of our students' knowledge of mathematics rather than their ability to memorize facts and procedures. These alternative methods of assessment offer students the opportunity to display how they approach problem situations, collect and organize information, formulate and test conjectures, and communicate their mathematical insights.

An authentic assessment program contains tasks that are appropriate to the topics the students are learning and that provide outcomes that are valuable to the students. Such an assessment program allows for such highly individual factors as a school's curriculum objectives, a teacher's style of instruction, and a student's maturity level and preferred learning style. Each individual teacher determines the assessment program best suited to the needs of his or her students.

> **In an instructional environment that demands a deeper understanding of mathematics, testing instruments that call for only identification of single correct responses no longer suffice. Instead, our instruments must reflect the scope and intent of our instructional program to have students solve problems, reason, and communicate.**
>
> *NCTM Standar*

To help a teacher select the most appropriate evaluation tools for his or her classroom, this *Assessment Sourcebook* provides the following materials. (See pre-chapter pages in *Transition Mathematics* Teacher's Edition for correlation of test items to chapter objectives.)

Assessment Forms

- student-completed forms
- teacher-completed forms for individual, group, and class activities

Assessment Instruments

- **Chapter Quizzes,** two per chapter, which cover three or four lessons and which contain mostly free-response items
- **Chapter Tests, Forms A and B,** which are alternate versions of each other and which test every chapter objective in primarily free-response format
- **Chapter Tests, Form C,** which consist of 4 to 6 performance-based, open-ended items, many of which assess several chapter objectives
- **Chapter Tests, Form D,** which are performance based and which often assess 5 or more chapter objectives as applied to a single larger task
- **Chapter Tests, Cumulative Form,** which contain mostly free-response items
- **Comprehensive Tests,** every three or four chapters, which are cumulative in nature and consist primarily of multiple-choice items

assess development of a student's
thematical power, a teacher needs to
e a mixture of means: essays,
mework, projects, short answers,
izzes, blackboard work, journals, oral
erviews, and group projects.

*Everybody Counts:
A Report to the Nation on the Future
of Mathematics Education*

uidelines for Developing an
uthentic Assessment Program

veloping an authentic program of assessment
n ongoing process. Some assessment
truments will seem perfectly suited to the
cher and his or her students from the start.
ers may be effective only after the teacher has
a chance to experiment, and refine them. Still
ers may be inappropriate for a given class or
tructional situation. The following are some
delines that may be helpful when choosing the
es of assessment for a particular program.

sessment serves many purposes.

or the teacher, assessment yields feedback on
e appropriateness of instructional methods
nd offers some clues as to how the content or
ace of instruction could be modified.

or the students, assessment should not only
dentify areas for improvement, but it should
lso affirm their successes.

raditional forms of assessment yield a
angible score.

ke the assessment process a positive
perience for students.

Jse a variety of assessment techniques.

rovide opportunities for students to
emonstrate their mathematical capabilities in
n atmosphere that encourages maximum
erformance.

mphasize what students *do* know and *can* do,
ot what they do not know and cannot do.

Motivate students to achieve by using tasks
hat reflect the value of their efforts.

Authentic assessment focuses on higher-order thinking skills.

○ Provides a picture of the student as a critical
  thinker and problem solver

○ Identifies *how* the student does mathematics,
  not just what answer he or she gets

Provide assessment activities that
resemble day-to-day tasks.

○ Use activities similar to instructional activities
  to assess.

○ Use assessment activities to further instruction.

○ Give students the immediate and detailed
  feedback they need to further the learning
  process.

○ Encourage students to explore how the
  mathematics they are learning applies to real
  situations.

Include each student as a partner in the
assessment process.

○ Encourage students to reflect on what they
  have done.

○ Encourage students to share their goals.

v

Portfolios and Notebooks

A portfolio is a collection of a student's work—projects, reports, drawings, reflections, representative assignments, assessment instruments—that displays the student's mathematical accomplishments over an extended period. The following suggestions for use should be adapted to the needs and organizational style of each situation.

A student notebook should reflect the student's day-to-day activities related to the mathematics class. It may include a section for journal entries as well as sections for homework, tests, and notes.

Getting Started

○ Provide file folders labeled *Portfolio*.
○ Provide guidelines for notebook format.

The Portfolio

○ The Portfolio can be used as the basis for assessing a student's achievements. The focus of the Portfolio should be on student thinking, growth in understanding over time, making mathematical connections, positive attitudes about mathematics, and the problem-solving process.

The Notebook

○ The notebook is for "work in progress." The student should keep in it all class and reading notes, group work, homework, reports and projects, and various student assessment forms, such as *Student Self-Assessment*.
○ Every two to six weeks students review their notebooks to determine the materials they would like to transfer to their Portfolios.
○ The teacher also selects student materials for the Portfolio and includes any appropriate assessment instruments.
○ The student completes the *About My Portfolio* form.

> **The opportunity to share mathematical ideas through portfolios can mark a real turning point in student attitudes.**
>
> *Mathematics Assessment (NCTM Publicatio*

○ Portfolios may include:

   student selected items from the notebook; a letter from the student about the work; a math autobiography; other work selected by the teacher including math surveys; various assessment documents.

Evaluating a Portfolio

○ Keep in mind that portfolio evaluation is a matter of ongoing discussion.
○ Set aside time to discuss the Portfolio with the student.
○ Use the Portfolio when discussing the student progress with his or her family.
○ Use it as a basis for identifying strengths and weaknesses and for setting goals for the next block of work.
○ Consider developing your own criteria for evaluating portfolios, for example, numeric scales.

Evaluating a Notebook

○ Notebooks should be evaluated based on agreed-upon guidelines.
○ Notebooks should be evaluated for organization and neatness, completeness, and timeliness.
○ Notebooks may be evaluated every week, every chapter, or any time you feel is appropriate.
○ You may choose to evaluate notebooks by checking items or by assigning numeric value to specific items.

sing Free-Response and Multiple-Choice Tests

.chers use written tests for many purposes.
.ticularly when it is objective-referenced, a test
 be a relatively quick and efficient method of
gnosing the scope of a student's mathematical
wledge. Tests can also provide valuable
.ructional feedback. And, of course, grades are
.aditional instrument for reporting student
.ievement to parents, administrators, and the
.nmunity. This *Sourcebook* provides a large
.nber of both free-response and multiple-
.ice items.

e-Response Tests

ree-response test, sometimes called a
.npletion test, is a collection of items for which
.udent must supply requested information.
.iile free-response tests are generally designed
 written responses, they may also be used
lly with individual students, especially those
.h limited English proficiency.

ltiple-choice Tests

.nultiple-choice test consists of many well-
.ined problems or questions. The student is
.en a set of four or five possible answers for
.h item and is asked to select the correct or best
.wer. The other choices, often called
.tractors, usually reflect common
.sconceptions or errors.

This *Sourcebook* contains:

○ Quizzes covering three or four lessons in each
  chapter. The quizzes are primarily free
  response in nature.

○ Chapter Tests, Forms A and B, which are
  alternate forms of each other and which test
  every chapter objective. The tests contain
  primarily free-response items, but they may
  also include several multiple-choice items.
  These tests can be used as chapter pretests and
  posttests to help implement needed
  individualized instruction.

○ Chapter Tests, Cumulative Form, for Chapters
  2-12, which are basically free-response
  assessment

○ Comprehensive Tests for Chapters 1-3, 1-6,
  1-9, and 1-13, which consist of mostly
  multiple-choice items and are cumulative
  in nature

Using Performance Assessment

In order to provide more authentic forms of assessment, this *Sourcebook* provides two forms of chapter tests that focus on students' ability to demonstrate their understanding of mathematical concepts.

Chapter Tests, Form C

The Form C Chapter Test items help you make a judgment of the students' understanding of mathematical concepts and their ability to interpret information, make generalizations, and communicate their ideas. Each assessment contains four to six open-ended questions, each of which is keyed to several chapter objectives.

Administering Form C Tests

The tests can be administered in a way that is b suited for the students. Provide manipulatives, extra paper, and other tools as needed. The use calculators is assumed.

○ Use all the assessment items.

○ Use only one or two, along with a free-respor or a multiple-choice test.

○ Use the assessment items to interview each student.

○ Have students give the explanations orally, a then write the answers.

Evaluating Form C Tests

Each test item is accompanied by a list of two c more evaluation criteria that can be used as a basis for judging student responses.

To rate how well students meet each criterion, a simple scale such as this may be used.

+ excellent
✓ satisfactory
− inadequate

Evaluation Guides for these tests are found starting on page 214 of this *Sourcebook*.

Comparison of Form C Tests and Free-Response Tests

	Form C Tests	Free Response Tests
Number of items	4–6	15–35
Sample Format	○ Draw 3 different rectangles that each have an area of 12 square centimeters.	○ Find the area of a rectangle that is 4 centimeters long and 3 centimeters wide.
Mode of administration	○ Interview ○ Written response ○ Combination of interview and written responses	○ Written response
Answers	○ May have more than one ○ May require an explanation by student	○ Single, short
Scoring	○ 2–4 evaluation criteria given ○ Use of simple rating scale	○ One correct answer for each item
Benefits	○ More accurate determination of instructional needs and strengths of students	○ Easy to score

Chapter Tests, Form D

The Form D Chapter Tests in this *Sourcebook* are composed of large mathematical tasks which allow students to demonstrate a broad spectrum of their abilities:

○ how they reason through difficult problems;

○ how they make and test conjectures;

○ how their number sense helps them give reasonable answers;

○ how they utilize alternative strategies.

These performance tasks also give teachers a means of assessing qualities of imagination, creativity, and perseverance.

Administering Form D Tests

Some Classroom Management Tips

Whenever possible, use Form D Tests as cooperative group activities, listening as students interact in their groups.	○ Have any needed mathematical tools or manipulatives readily available. The use of calculators is assumed.
Ask students questions that will give you information about their thought processes.	○ Be sure all students understand the purpose of the task. Offer assistance as needed.

Evaluating Performance Assessments

For each assessment, a set of task-specific performance standards provides a means for judging the quality of the students' work. These standards identify five levels of performance related to the particular task. The specific standards were created using the following characteristics of student performance as general guidelines.

Level 5: Accomplishes and extends the task; displays in-depth understanding; communicates effectively and completely.

Level 4: Accomplishes the task competently; displays clear understanding of key concepts; communicates effectively.

Level 3: Substantially completes the task; displays minor flaws in understanding or technique; communicates successfully.

Level 2: Only partially completes the task; displays one or more major errors in understanding or technique; communicates unclear or incomplete information.

Level 1: Attempts the task, but fails to complete it in any substantive way; displays only fragmented understanding; attempts communication, but is not successful.

Each test is accompanied by a set of teacher notes that identifies the chapter objectives being assessed, as well as the mathematical concepts and skills involved in the performance task. The notes also list any materials that are needed and provide answers where appropriate. Questions to guide students as they seek solutions are provided, along with ideas for extending the activity. These notes, along with the performance standards as described at the left, are found in the Evaluation Guides starting on page 215 of this *Sourcebook*.

Since performance tasks are open-ended, student responses are as varied and individual as the students themselves. For this reason, it may be helpful to use these general guidelines as well as the task-specific standards when determining the level of each student's performance.

Using Assessment Forms

Using Student-Completed Forms

To do meaningful work in our fast-paced and ever-changing technological world, students must learn to assess their own progress. This *Sourcebook* provides four forms that can be used to help students with self-assessment. Use one or more depending on the needs of your students.

Using Teacher-Completed Forms

This *Sourcebook* also provides ten assessment forms that are designed to help you keep a record of authentic assessments. Some forms are for use with individual students, while others are for use with groups of students. Determine which would be best suited for use in your classroom.

	Form	Purpose	Suggested Uses
Student-Completed	*Student Survey*	Checklist of student attitudes toward various math activities	○ Periodically monitor the change in student attitudes toward math
	Student Self-Assessment	Checklist of student awareness of how well he or she works independently	○ Monitor student progress in working independently
	Cooperative Groups Self-Assessment	Form for students to describe their attitudes and interaction with other students in a cooperative-learning situation	○ Completed at the conclusion of group learning activities ○ Completed by individual student or groups of students
	About My Portfolio	Form for student to describe the contents of his or her portfolio	○ Completed when student transfers work from the notebook to the *Portfolio*
Teacher-Completed	*Portfolio Assessment*	Form to assess student's mathematical accomplishments over time	○ Use to discuss student's progress in discussions with family
	Notebooks, Individual Assessment	Form to record student's organizational skills and completeness of assignments	○ Describe student's attention to specified daily tasks
	Notebooks, Class Checklist	Checklist to record students' notebook maintenance	○ Use when setting goals for improving study skills
	Problem Solving, Individual Assessment	Form to assess each student in a problem-solving situation	○ Describe level of student performance ○ Modify the level to meet individual needs
	Problem Solving, Class Checklist	Checklist to assess groups of students in problem-solving situations	○ Assess the entire class ○ Assess small groups over time
	Observation, Individual Assessment	Form to determine the student's thought processes, performances, and attitudes	○ Record observation of student in classroom
	Observation, Class Checklist	Checklist for observing several students at one time	○ Provide a mathematical profile of the entire class ○ Identify common strengths and weaknesses ○ Help in modifying content or pace and in determining appropriate groupings.
	Cooperative Groups, Class Checklist	Checklist to assess students' abilities to work constructively in groups	○ Assess one or more cooperative groups
	Project Assessment	Form for evaluating extended projects or oral presentations	○ Evaluate an individual or group project or presentation ○ Prepare students for presentations or projects
	Overall Student Assessment, Class Checklist	Checklist summary of students' overall performance	○ Evaluate student performance over an entire instructional period

Student Survey

Answer the following questions using the rating scale provided.

5   Always
4   Usually
3   Sometimes
2   Rarely
1   Never

_____   **1.** I read material more than once if I don't understand it.

_____   **2.** I use the reading heads and bold terms to help me preview the material.

_____   **3.** I review for a test more than one day before it is given.

_____   **4.** I concentrate when I study.

_____   **5.** I try all the examples.

_____   **6.** I do all of my assigned homework.

_____   **7.** I pay attention in class.

_____   **8.** I take notes and keep my notebook up-to-date and neat.

_____   **9.** I bring the required materials to class.

_____   **10.** I really try to get good grades.

_____   **11.** I ask questions and try to get help when I need it.

_____   **12.** I use the Progress Self-Test and Chapter Review to prepare for tests.

_____   **13.** I make up work when I have been absent.

_____   **14.** I look for uses of math in real life.

_____   **15.** I can solve most problems.

_____   **16.** I like to try new strategies.

_____   **17.** I give up too easily.

_____   **18.** I work cooperatively.

My favorite kind of math is _____

because _____

List some activities in which you have used math.

_____

_____

_____

Student Self-Assessment

Assignment _____

Complete the following sentences to describe your learning experience.

I was supposed to learn _____

_____

I started the work by _____

_____

_____

As a group member, I contributed _____

_____

_____

I learned _____

_____

_____

I am still confused by _____

_____

_____

I enjoyed the assignment because _____

_____

_____

I think the assignment was worthwhile because _____

_____

_____

Check the sentences that describe your work on this assignment.

☐ I was able to do the work.
☐ I did not understand the directions.
☐ I followed the directions but got wrong answers.
☐ I can explain how to do this assignment to someone else.
☐ The assignment was easier than I thought it would be.
☐ The assignment was harder than I thought it would be.

Cooperative Groups Self-Assessment

Assignment _____

Reader: _____   Writer: _____

Materials handler: _____   Checker: _____

Others in group: _____

Materials: _____

Check the sentences that describe your work.

☐ We had a new idea or made a suggestion.
☐ We asked for more information.
☐ We shared the information we found.
☐ We tried different ways to solve the problem.
☐ We helped others explain their ideas better.
☐ We pulled our ideas together.
☐ We were reminded to work together.
☐ We demonstrated a knowledge of the mathematical concept.
☐ We encouraged those who did not understand.

Complete each sentence.

We learned

_____

_____

We found an answer by

_____

_____

After we found an answer, we

_____

_____

By working together, we

_____

_____

About My Portfolio

Complete the following sentences about the work you are putting into your portfolio.
Describe the assignment.

_____

_____

_____

I chose this work as part of my portfolio because

_____

_____

_____

I began my work by

_____

_____

_____

Doing this work helped me

_____

_____

_____

The work was ☐ too easy ☐ easy ☐ just right ☐ hard ☐ too hard

because _____

_____

_____

Portfolio Assessment

The work in this portfolio:

shows growth in the student's mathematical understanding.

exhibits the student's ability to reason mathematically.

makes connections within mathematics.

makes connections to other disciplines.

shows that the student is able to work on mathematical tasks in cooperative groups.

illustrates the appropriate use of a variety of tools.

Notebooks   **Individual Assessment**

Rate items, based upon your requirements, as follows:
+   if excellent
✓   if satisfactory
-    if needs improvement
NA   if not applicable

Written Assignments   **Comments**

_____ **1.** Assignment sheet

_____ **2.** Daily homework

_____ **3.** Lesson Warm-ups

_____ **4.** Lesson Masters

_____ **5.** Activities

_____ **6.** Projects

Reading and Class Notes   **Comments**

_____ **7.** Definitions

_____ **8.** Properties

_____ **9.** Examples

_____ **10.** Class notes, handouts

Assessment   **Comments**

_____ **11.** Chapter Quizzes

_____ **12.** Chapter Progress Self-Test

_____ **13.** Chapter Review

_____ **14.** Chapter Tests

_____ **15.** Cumulative Chapter Test

_____ **16.** Comprehensive Test

Other   **Comments**

_____ **17.**

_____ **18.**

_____ **19.**

_____ **20.**

Overall Rating/Comments

_____

_____

Notebooks

Class

Rate each item as follows:
+   if excellent
✓   if satisfactory
-     if needs improvement
NA   if not applicable

Students	Date	Written Assignments		Reading/Class Notes		Assessment			
1.									
2.									
3.									
4.									
5.									
6.									
7.									
8.									
9.									
10.									
11.									
12.									
13.									
14.									
15.									
16.									
17.									
18.									
19.									
20.									
21.									
22.									
23.									
24.									
25.									
26.									
27.									
28.									
29.									
30.									

Problem Solving

Check each statement below that accurately describes the student's work. This list includes suggested student behaviors to consider. Feel free to modify it to suit your needs.

Reads carefully   **Comments**

☐ Looks up unfamiliar words
☐ Understands lesson concepts and can apply
   them
☐ Rereads
☐ Finds/uses information appropriately
☐
☐

Creates a plan   **Comments**

☐ Chooses an appropriate strategy
☐ Estimates the answer
☐
☐
☐

Carries out the plan   **Comments**

☐ Works systematically and with care
☐ Shows work in an organized fashion
☐ Computes correctly
☐ Rereads the problem if the first attempt is
   unsuccessful
☐ Rereads the problem and interprets the solution
☐ States the answer in required format
☐
☐
☐

Checks the work   **Comments**

☐ Checks by estimating
☐ Tries alternate approaches
☐
☐
☐

Problem Solving

Class _____

Rate each item as follows:
+   if excellent
✓   if satisfactory
-     if needs improvement
NA   if not applicable

Students	Date	Looks up unfamiliar words	Understands the question/task	Uses information appropriately	Chooses an appropriate strategy	Estimates the answer	Is systematic and careful	Computes correctly	Rereads the problem if necessary	States answer in required format	Tries alternate approaches
1.											
2.											
3.											
4.											
5.											
6.											
7.											
8.											
9.											
10.											
11.											
12.											
13.											
14.											
15.											
16.											
17.											
18.											
19.											
20.											
21.											
22.											
23.											
24.											
25.											
26.											
27.											
28.											
29.											
30.											

Observation

	Usually	Sometimes	Rarely
Understanding			
Demonstrates knowledge of skills	☐	☐	☐
Understands concepts	☐	☐	☐
Selects appropriate solution strategies	☐	☐	☐
Solves problems accurately	☐	☐	☐
Work Habits			
Works in an organized manner	☐	☐	☐
Works neatly	☐	☐	☐
Submits work on time	☐	☐	☐
Works well with others	☐	☐	☐
Uses time productively	☐	☐	☐
Asks for help when needed	☐	☐	☐
Confidence			
Initiates questions	☐	☐	☐
Displays positive attitude	☐	☐	☐
Helps others	☐	☐	☐
Flexibility			
Tries alternative approaches	☐	☐	☐
Considers and uses ideas of others	☐	☐	☐
Like to try alternative methods	☐	☐	☐
Perseverance			
Shows patience and perseverance	☐	☐	☐
Works systematically	☐	☐	☐
Is willing to try	☐	☐	☐
Checks work regularly	☐	☐	☐
Other			
_____	☐	☐	☐
_____	☐	☐	☐
_____	☐	☐	☐

Observation

Class

Rate each item as follows:
+   if excellent
✓   if satisfactory
-    if needs improvement
NA   if not applicable

Students	Date	Demonstrates knowledge of skills	Understands concepts	Works neatly and systematically	Works well with others	Asks for help when needed	Uses time productively	Displays positive attitude	Tries alternative approaches	Considers and uses ideas of others	Shows patience and perseverance
1.											
2.											
3.											
4.											
5.											
6.											
7.											
8.											
9.											
10.											
11.											
12.											
13.											
14.											
15.											
16.											
17.											
18.											
19.											
20.											
21.											
22.											
23.											
24.											
25.											
26.											
27.											
28.											
29.											
30.											

Cooperative Groups

Class

Rate each item as follows:
+   if excellent
✓   if satisfactory
-     if needs improvement
NA   if not applicable

Students	Date	Works with others in the group	Considers and uses ideas of others	Tutors and helps others	Has a positive attitude	Disagrees but is not disagreeable	Shows patience and perseverance	Works systematically	Initiates questions			
1.												
2.												
3.												
4.												
5.												
6.												
7.												
8.												
9.												
10.												
11.												
12.												
13.												
14.												
15.												
16.												
17.												
18.												
19.												
20.												
21.												
22.												
23.												
24.												
25.												
26.												
27.												
28.												
29.												
30.												

Name _____   *Date* _____

Project Assessment

Project _____

Rate each item as follows:
+   if excellent
✓   if satisfactory
-    if needs improvement
NA   if not applicable

The Project

_____ Demonstrates mathematical concepts properly

_____ Communicates ideas clearly

_____ Shows connection to another subject

_____ Shows evidence of time spent in planning and preparation

_____ Is original and creative

_____ Includes charts, tables, and/or graphs where appropriate

_____ Uses available technology effectively

_____ Stimulates further investigation of the topic

_____ Includes a short written report if the project is a model or demonstration

_____ Lists resources used

The Oral Presentation

_____ Is organized (includes an introduction, main section, and conclusion)

_____ Uses audio-visual materials where appropriate

_____ Speaks clearly and paces presentation properly

_____ Answers questions and stimulates further interest among classmates

_____ Holds audience's attention

Overall Project Rating/Comments

_____

_____

_____

_____

Overall Student Assessment

Class Checklist

Class

Rate each item as follows:

+	if excellent
✓	if satisfactory
-	if needs improvement
NA	if not applicable

Students	Date	Class Work	Discussion	Cooperative Groups	Problem Solving	Homework	Notebooks	Projects	Tests		
1.											
2.											
3.											
4.											
5.											
6.											
7.											
8.											
9.											
10.											
11.											
12.											
13.											
14.											
15.											
16.											
17.											
18.											
19.											
20.											
21.											
22.											
23.											
24.											
25.											
26.											
27.											
28.											
29.											
30.											

QUIZ

1. In 1991, there were 605,694 live births in the state of California.

   a. What is the count?

   1. a. _____

   b. What is the counting unit?

   b. _____

2. In decimal notation, write the number that is one less than ten million.

   2. _____

3. Order from smallest to largest: 4.3   4.03   4.34

   3. _____

4. Write a number between 21.3 and 21.4.

   4. _____

5. Consider this drawing:

   |—+—+—+—+—+—+—+—+—+—+—|

   a. How many intervals are pictured?

   5. a. _____

   b. How many tick marks are used?

   b. _____

6. Use the number line drawn here.

   A B C D E F G H I
   ◄—+—+—+—+—+—+—+—+—+—►
     10   12   14

   a. What is the length of each interval?

   6. a. _____

   b. Which letter corresponds to the number 11.5?

   b. _____

7. Round 0.747

   a. up to the next hundredth.

   7. a. _____

   b. down to the preceding hundredth.

   b. _____

   c. to the nearest hundredth.

   c. _____

8. *Multiple choice.* A number rounded to the nearest hundredth is 3.61. What number *cannot* be the original number?

   8. _____

   (a) 3.61   (b) 3.607

   (c) 3.614   (d) 3.6

9. You beat the school record of 13.8 seconds for the 100-meter dash by six tenths of a second. What was your time?

   9. _____

10. Describe what a calculator does when it truncates a number. Use an example to illustrate.

    _____

    _____

QUIZ

Lessons 1-5 Through 1-8

In 1 and 2, find a decimal for the fraction.

1. $\frac{21}{8}$

2. $\frac{7}{11}$

3. In the fraction $\frac{136}{17}$, name

    a. the dividend.

    b. the quotient.

    c. the divisor.

4. Write a number that is greater than 150 and divisible by 19.

In 5 and 6, write a calculator key sequence to find a decimal equal to the number.

5. $\frac{49}{63}$

6. $-9 + 16 - 20$

7. Name a number that is less than -7.

In 8 and 9, order from smallest to largest.

8. $\frac{33}{50}$ $\frac{2}{3}$ $\frac{3}{5}$

9. $-2\frac{3}{16}$ $-2\frac{2}{11}$ $-2\frac{1}{5}$

In 10–12, write an integer for each situation.

10. losing four pounds

11. depositing $50 in a savings account

12. a profit of $100

13. Explain in your own words what an integer is. Include examples that will justify your explanation.

1. _____

2. _____

3. a. _____

   b. _____

   c. _____

4. _____

5. _____

6. _____

7. _____

8. _____

9. _____

10. _____

11. _____

12. _____

_____

_____

CHAPTER 1 TEST, Form A

1. In 1991, the Detroit Tigers won eighty-four games.

    a. What is the count?

    b. What is the counting unit?

2. In 1675.342, which digit is

    a. in the thousands place?

    b. in the hundredths place?

3. What digit is in the millionths place of π?

4. Write as a decimal: thirty-one thousand six.

5. Write 60.09 in words.

6. What is the smallest six-digit whole number?

7. Eight cans of juice are advertised at $1.90. If you divide 1.90 by 8 on your calculator, the display is $\boxed{0.2375}$. What will be the cost for one can?

8. *Multiple choice.* Which of the following is *not* equal to eight?

    (a) $\frac{8}{1}$ (b) $\frac{48}{6}$ (c) $\frac{80}{10}$ (d) $\frac{0}{8}$

9. List all integers between -2 and 3.

In 10 and 11, use the number line at the right.

10. What is the length of each interval?

11. Give the number that corresponds to

    a. letter *A*.

    b. letter *B*.

    c. letter *C*.

12. Name a number that is greater than -2 and less than zero.

1. a. _____

   b. _____

2. a. _____

   b. _____

3. _____

4. _____

5. _____

6. _____

7. _____

8. _____

9. _____

A   B   C

-6.4   -5.6   -4.8

10. _____

11. a. _____

    b. _____

    c. _____

12. _____

13. Use $<$ twice with 3.12, $3.\overline{1}$, and .31 in a single sentence.

13. _____

14. Write as a mathematical sentence using a $>$ or $<$ sign: Owing \$15 is worse than owing \$5.

14. _____

15. Round 247.83 to the nearest tenth.

15. _____

16. Round 247.83 up to the next whole number.

16. _____

17. Round 247.83 down to the preceding ten.

17. _____

18. Round $5 \times \pi$ to the nearest integer.

18. _____

19. In the division $\dfrac{3}{43.7}$, which number should you key in first on your calculator?

19. _____

20. Find a number between $\frac{2}{3}$ and $\frac{5}{6}$.

20. _____

21. Find a number between 13.4 and 13.5.

21. _____

22. Write $\frac{33}{16}$ as a decimal.

22. _____

23. Write $12\frac{5}{11}$ as a decimal.

23. _____

24. Write $28.1\overline{6}$ as a fraction in lowest terms.

24. _____

25. What digit is in the seventh decimal place in $.\overline{31}$?

25. _____

26. Which is smaller, $2\frac{6}{7}$ or $2\frac{7}{8}$?

26. _____

27. Graph -3.75 on the number line.

27.

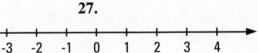

28. Write a fraction with 8 in the numerator and 17 in the denominator, and write another fraction equal to it.

28. _____

29. Which number is the largest: $\frac{59}{99}$, $\frac{1}{2}$, or $\frac{14}{25}$?

29. _____

30. Rewrite $\frac{24}{72}$ in lowest terms.

30. _____

31. Rewrite $7\frac{18}{27}$ in lowest terms.

31. _____

32. What number is ten less than one million?

32. _____

In 33 and 34, use this information: A town's population rounded to the nearest hundred is 1000.

33. What is the smallest possible actual population?

33. _____

34. What is the largest possible actual population?

34. _____

35. How many tick marks are needed to divide a segment into eight intervals?

35. _____

36. *Multiple choice.* From what country was the person who first used the *slash* for fractions?

36. _____

  (a) America   (b) Egypt

  (c) Greece   (d) Mexico

37. List all factors of the numerator of $\frac{51}{72}$.

37. _____

38. Find the greatest common factor of the numerator and denominator of $\frac{64}{96}$.

38. _____

39. An explorer starts at sea level, descends 76 feet, and climbs upward 59 feet. What is the explorer's new elevation?

39. _____

40. Write an explanation of how you would estimate the cost of 3 compact discs at $12.99 each.

_____

_____

_____

Now check all your work carefully.

CHAPTER 1 TEST, Form B

1. The Pentagon in Arlington, Virginia, contains 7,748 windows.

   a. What is the count?

   b. What is the counting unit?

   1. a. _____

   b. _____

2. In 38,257.9164, which digit is

   a. in the thousands place?

   b. in the hundredths place?

   2. a. _____

   b. _____

3. What digit is in the ten-thousandths place of π?

   3. _____

4. Write as a decimal: forty thousand five.

   4. _____

5. Write the word name for 52.07.

   5. _____

6. What is the largest four-digit whole number?

   6. _____

7. T-shirts are on sale at three for $29. If you divide 29 by 3 on your calculator, the display is $\boxed{9.66666667}$. What is the cost for one shirt?

   7. _____

8. *Multiple choice.* Which of the following is *not* equal to 7?

   (a) $\frac{7}{1}$ 　　 (b) $\frac{21}{3}$ 　　 (c) $\frac{0}{7}$ 　　 (d) $\frac{14}{2}$

   8. _____

9. List all integers between -3 and 4.

   9. _____

In 10 and 11, use the number line at the right.

A 　 B 　 C 　 D

7.2 　 8

10. What is the length of each interval?

    10. _____

11. Give the number that corresponds to

    a. letter *A*.

    b. letter *C*.

    c. letter *D*.

    11. a. _____

    b. _____

    c. _____

12. Name a number that is less than -1 and greater than -2.

    12. _____

13. Use > twice with -4.1, .41, and -41 in a single sentence.

13. _____

14. Write as a math sentence using a > or < sign: Losing by 5 points is a better showing than losing by 16 points.

14. _____

15. Round 105.74 to the nearest tenth.

15. _____

16. Round 105.74 up to the next whole number.

16. _____

17. Round 105.74 down to the preceding ten.

17. _____

18. Round the product $\pi \times \pi$ to the nearest integer.

18. _____

19. In the division $\frac{4}{23.1}$, which number should you key in first on your calculator?

19. _____

20. Find a number between $\frac{1}{4}$ and $\frac{1}{5}$.

20. _____

21. Find a number between 6.2 and 6.3.

21. _____

22. Write $\frac{3}{16}$ as a decimal.

22. _____

23. Write $16\frac{2}{3}$ as a decimal.

23. _____

24. Write $.8\overline{3}$ as a fraction in lowest terms.

24. _____

25. What is the digit in the fifth decimal place in $.\overline{27}$?

25. _____

26. Which is smaller, $3\frac{2}{5}$ or $3\frac{1}{9}$?

26. _____

27. Graph -2.5 on the number line.

27.

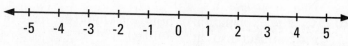

28. Write a fraction with 7 in the numerator and 12 in the denominator, and write another fraction equal to it.

28. _____

29. Which number is the largest: $\frac{37}{50}$, $\frac{13}{18}$, or $\frac{19}{25}$?

29. _____

30. Rewrite $\frac{16}{48}$ in lowest terms.

30. _____

31. Rewrite $8\frac{15}{21}$ in lowest terms.

31. _____

32. What number is four less than one million?

32. _____

In 33 and 34, use this information: A town's population rounded to the nearest hundred is 900.

33. What is the smallest possible actual population?

33. _____

34. What is the largest possible actual population?

34. _____

35. How many tick marks are needed to divide a segment into ten intervals?

35. _____

36. *Multiple choice.* What people first used the fraction bar?

36. _____

    (a) Arabs   (b) Chinese

    (c) Greeks   (d) Mexicans

37. List all factors of the denominator of $\frac{27}{48}$.

37. _____

38. Find the greatest common factor of the numerator and denominator of $\frac{32}{72}$.

38. _____

39. The price of a $69.45 tire is lowered $5.75 for a sale. After the sale, the price is raised $6.15. What is the new price?

39. _____

40. Write an explanation of how you would estimate the cost of 4 compact discs at $13.99 each.

40. _____

_____

_____

_____

Now check all your work carefully.

Name

CHAPTER 1 TEST, Form C

1. Use your calculator. Determine a way to fill in the boxes below with the digits 5, 6, 7, 8, 9, and 0 to make a product that is between 30 and 40. (You may use each digit only once.) What is your product?

$\square . \square\square \times \square\square . \square$

2. Describe a real situation in which it is appropriate to round a decimal *up* and a different situation when it is appropriate to round a decimal *down*. Give specific examples to show how you would round the decimals involved.

3. Make a drawing to show why the following statement is true.

$$\frac{2}{3} = \frac{4}{6} = \frac{6}{9}$$

4. What numbers do you think are represented by points *A* and *B* on the number line below? Explain your reasoning.

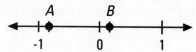

5. Explain why the decimals 0.16, $0.1\overline{6}$, and $0.\overline{16}$ are not equal to the same number. Then use these three decimals to fill in the blanks in the following expression.

_____ > _____ > _____

6. Your friend was absent from school for a few days and has asked you to explain how to convert fractions and mixed numbers to decimals. How would you explain what to do? Tell your friend about the decimals and fractions you should know from memory.

CHAPTER 1 TEST, Form D

Your family is planning a two-week vacation next summer. The destinations you are considering are Orlando, Florida; Washington, D.C.; and San Francisco, California. Whichever choice your family makes, your parents hope to drive there in the family car. They have asked for your help in estimating the total cost of the trip.

At the library, you find an automobile travel guide and an atlas. The travel guide contains the list of travel expenses shown at the right. In the atlas, you find the following distances between your city and the three possible vacation cities.

Orlando, Florida	1122 miles
Washington, D.C.	869 miles
San Francisco, California	1443 miles

a. Choose your favorite vacation city from those listed above. What amount do you think you should budget for highway tolls on a *round trip* to that city?

b. In highway driving, the family car can travel about 36 miles on a gallon of gasoline. About how much gasoline do you think you will need on a round trip to the city you chose? About how much will that gasoline cost?

c. What do you think will be the total cost of a trip for a family of four to the city you chose? Make a budget that shows separate estimates for all major expenses. Be sure to show how you arrived at each estimate.

d. Your parents plan to put aside some money for the vacation each month for the next year. What amount do you think this should be? Explain.

Summer Travel
How much can you expect to spend on your summer vacation? If you are traveling by automobile within the United States, here is a list of some current costs.

Hotel/Motel
from $80 to $105 per night for a family of four

Food
about $15 to $20 per day per person

Gasoline
from $.99 to $1.19 per gallon

Highway Tolls
from 1¢ to 2¢ per mile

In addition, be sure to consider admission fees for museums, theme parks, and so on. Fees for theme parks, in particular, can be a considerable expense, with some costing $100 or more per day for a family of four.

QUIZ

1. $3.26 \times 100{,}000$

1. _____

2. 0.07×10^7

2. _____

3. In 4^3,

   a. what is the 3 called?

   3. a. _____

   b. what is the 4 called?

   b. _____

4. Which is larger: 5^6 or 6^5?

4. _____

5. *Multiple choice.* Which of these numbers is written in scientific notation?

   (a) 35×10^3 (b) 3.5×10^4

   (c) $.35 \times 10^5$ (d) 3.5×100^2

5. _____

6. In 1991 the federal budget for the United States totaled $1.32 trillion.

   a. Write this number as a decimal.

   6. a. _____

   b. Write this number in scientific notation.

   b. _____

7. Your calculator display reads $\boxed{3.072 \qquad 08}$.

   What decimal is represented?

7. _____

For 8 and 9, use this information: The largest man-made reservoir in the U.S., Lake Mead, was formed with the construction of Hoover Dam in 1936. It holds 34,850,000,000 cubic meters of water.

8. Write the key sequence to enter this number in your calculator.

8. _____

9. A cubic meter of water weighs 1000 kilograms. Write the weight of the water in Lake Mead as a decimal.

9. _____

10. Explain why scientific notation is useful.

_____

_____

_____

QUIZ

In 1-4, write each expression as a decimal.

1. $\frac{1}{1000} \times 34.7$

2. $600 \times .000001$

3. 30% of 200

4. 5.5% of 750

In 5-16, complete the chart. Write fractions or mixed numbers in lowest terms.

Fraction or Mixed Number	Decimal	Percent
$\frac{1}{4}$	**5.** ?	**6.** ?
7. ?	.085	**8.** ?
9. ?	**10.** ?	72%
11. ?	$.\overline{6}$	**12.** ?
$\frac{5}{12}$	**13.** ?	**14.** ?
15. ?	**16.** ?	$\frac{1}{2}$%

In 17 and 18, show any calculations that you do.

17. You just bought a $100 certificate of deposit which pays 4.29% interest annually. How much money will the CD be worth one year from now?

18. According to *USA Today,* June 23, 1993, a poll of 1021 women showed 66% of them don't exercise regularly. How many women is this?

1. _____

2. _____

3. _____

4. _____

5. _____

6. _____

7 _____

8. _____

9. _____

10. _____

11. _____

12 _____

13. _____

14. _____

15. _____

16. _____

17. _____

18. _____

CHAPTER 2 TEST, Form A

In 1-9, write each number as a decimal.

1. $10,000 \times 4.8$ 1. _____

2. $26 \times .001$ 2. _____

3. 3.95 million   3. _____

4. 5^4 4. _____

5. 7.6×10^7 5. _____

6. 26 millionths   6. _____

7. 2.9×10^{-5} 7. _____

8. $\boxed{4.28 \qquad\qquad 05}$ 8. _____

9. 8%   9. _____

10. According to the Substitution Principle,   10. _____

    $\frac{3}{4} - \frac{1}{2} = $ _____ ? _____ % $-$ _____ ? _____ %.   _____

In 11-13, write the word name for each number.

11. 6,000,000,000,000   11. _____

12. 10^{-5} 12. _____

13. 10^0 13. _____

In 14-17, write each in scientific notation.

14. 4,620,000   14. _____

15. 3 billion   15. _____

16. one hundred-thousandth   16. _____

17. 7.5 nanoseconds (billionths of a second)   17. _____

18. Write the expression 3^5 in words.   18. _____

19. Explain why 2.5×7^{10} is *not* in scientific notation.   19. _____

20. Which is larger: 6^4 or 4^6?

20. _____

21. Calculate: 0^{561}

21. _____

22. Rewrite $\frac{3.8}{19}$ as a simple fraction in lowest terms.

22. _____

23. How might Lloyd's of London's 1990 loss of $4,300,000,000 appear in a newspaper headline?

23. _____

24. What is a key sequence for entering 8.5 billion on your calculator?

24. _____

25. Write >, <, or = to make this statement true:

3.8×10^{-4} ___?___ 1.7×10^{-5}

25. _____

In 26 and 27, use the circle graph below.

Municipal Solid-Waste Generation in 1990

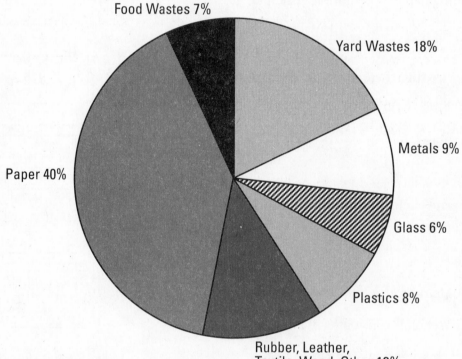

Food Wastes 7%

Yard Wastes 18%

Metals 9%

Paper 40%

Glass 6%

Plastics 8%

Rubber, Leather, Textile, Wood, Other 12%

26. What waste product has the

   a. largest volume of waste?

26. a. _____

   b. smallest volume of waste?

b. _____

27. What does the whole circle graph represent?

27. _____

Name _____

In 28, show your work.

28. You invest $7,500 in a certificate of deposit paying 3.78%   28. _____
    per year. How much interest will you earn the first year?

29. Consider the circle at
    the right.

    a. Name the center.

    b. Name the diameter.

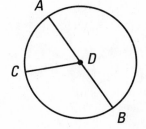

29. a. _____

    b. _____

30. Explain why very small numbers are often written in scientific notation.

    _____

    _____

    _____

In 31-40, complete the chart.

Fraction or Mixed Number (in lowest terms)	Decimal	Percent
$\frac{3}{4}$	31. ?	32. ?
33. ?	34. ?	45%
35. ?	$.\overline{3}$	36. ?
37. ?	38. ?	250%
39. ?	.005	40. ?

31. _____

32. _____

33. _____

34. _____

35. _____

36. _____

37. _____

38. _____

39. _____

40. _____

Now check all your work carefully.

15

CHAPTER 2 TEST, Form B

In 1-9, write each number as a decimal.

1. $5.75 \times 100{,}000$　　　　　　　　　　　　1. _____

2. $.01 \times 42$　　　　　　　　　　　　　　　　2. _____

3. 6.29 billion　　　　　　　　　　　　　　　　3. _____

4. 6^3　　　　　　　　　　　　　　　　　　　4. _____

5. 9.2×10^8　　　　　　　　　　　　　　5. _____

6. 26 millionths　　　　　　　　　　　　　　　6. _____

7. 2.9×10^{-5}　　　　　　　　　　　　　7. _____

8. $\boxed{6.29 \qquad -04}$　　　　　　　　　　8. _____

9. 8%　　　　　　　　　　　　　　　　　　　9. _____

10. According to the Substitution Principle,　　10. _____

$\frac{1}{5} + \frac{1}{2} =$ ___?___ % + ___?___ %.

_____

In 11-13, write the word name for each number.

11. 8,000,000　　　　　　　　　　　　　　　11. _____

12. 10^{-3}　　　　　　　　　　　　　　　　12. _____

13. 10^1　　　　　　　　　　　　　　　　　13. _____

In 14-17, write each in scientific notation.

14. 3,296,000,000　　　　　　　　　　　　　14. _____

15. 40 million　　　　　　　　　　　　　　　15. _____

16. one-thousandth　　　　　　　　　　　　　16. _____

17. 5 nanoseconds (billionths of a second)　　17. _____

18. Write the expression 4^3 in words.　　　　18. _____

19. Explain why 321×10^{-2} is *not* in scientific notation.　　19. _____

20. Which is larger: 5^6 or 6^5? 20. _____

21. Calculate: 1^{329} 21. _____

22. Rewrite $\frac{4.5}{9}$ as a simple fraction in lowest terms. 22. _____

23. How might the 1992 Alaska State Budget, $2,420,000,000, appear in a newspaper headline? 23. _____

24. What is a key sequence for entering 4.7 trillion on your calculator? 24. _____

25. Write >, <, or = to make the statement true: 25. _____
    1.8×10^{-5} ___?___ 4.26×10^{-6}

In 26 and 27, use the circle graph below.

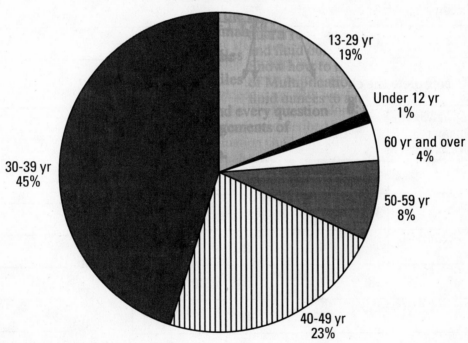

Distribution of AIDS Deaths, by Age: 1982 Through 1991
126,827 deaths

26. Which age group had
    a. the highest number of AIDS deaths? 26. a. _____

    b. the lowest number of AIDS deaths? b. _____

27. What does the whole circle graph represent? 27. _____

In 28, show your work.

28. In New York City, sales tax is $8\frac{1}{4}\%$. How much is the total bill for a CD priced at $14.94?

28. _____

29. Consider the circle at the right.

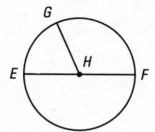

a. Name the center.

b. Name a radius.

29. a. _____

b. _____

30. Give two reasons for writing very large numbers in scientific notation.

_____

_____

_____

In 31-40, complete the chart.

Fraction or Mixed Number (in lowest terms)	Decimal	Percent
$\frac{3}{5}$	31. ?	32. ?
33. ?	34. ?	25%
35. ?	$.\overline{6}$	36. ?
37. ?	38. ?	310%
39. ?	.002	40. ?

31. _____

32. _____

33. _____

34. _____

35. _____

36. _____

37. _____

38. _____

39. _____

40. _____

Now check all your work carefully.

CHAPTER 2 TEST, Form C

1. Explain the differences among these three expressions.

   $$2 \times 10 \qquad 2^{10} \qquad 10^2$$

2. Suppose that the ⬚**0** key of your calculator is broken. How could you use the scientific notation key to display this number?

   1850000

3. Explain why this number is not written in scientific notation.

   $$47 \times 10^{-5}$$

   What is the correct scientific notation for the number?

4. Let n represent an amount of money. List the amounts that follow in order from least to greatest. Explain your reasoning.

   n 7.5% of n 75% of n 750% of n

5. Carla made this graph to show how she plans to use the $585 that she received as graduation gifts. About how much does she plan to spend on each item?

   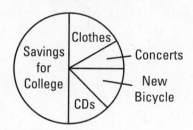

6. Explain why each step shown below is true.

   Step 1 $5\frac{1}{4}\% = 5.25\%$

   Step 2 $= 5.25 \times 0.01$

   Step 3 $= 0.0525$

CHAPTER 2 TEST, Form D

The students at Springfield Middle School collected data
regarding how they get to school in the morning. They were
asked to make circle graphs of their data. Each grade worked
separately, though, and they produced the three graphs shown
at the right. As you can see, the first graph is labeled with
fractions, the second is labeled with percents, and the third is
labeled with whole numbers.

You work after school in the school office. Your job
today is to adjust the graphs and summarize the data.

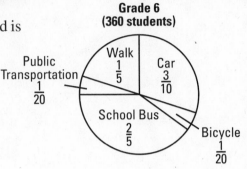

**Grade 6
(360 students)**

a. What kinds of numbers do you think
should be used to label the graphs:
percents, fractions, or whole
numbers? Explain your reasoning.

b. Trace the outlines of the three graphs onto
a separate sheet of paper, but do *not* copy
the labels. Using the method that you
chose in Part a, adjust the graphs so that all
three are labeled in the same way.

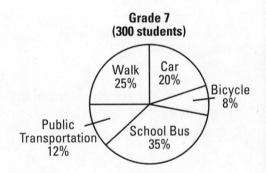

**Grade 7
(300 students)**

c. Use the data from the graphs. What is the
total number of students who walk to
school? What fraction of all the students is
this? What percent?

d. Make a table that shows *combined* data for
all three grades.

e. A *trend* is a pattern of change in data. The
principal has asked if you see any trends in
these data from grade to grade. Write a
brief report to answer the principal's
question.

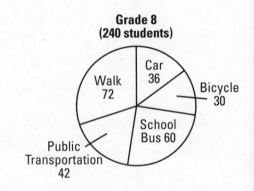

**Grade 8
(240 students)**

CHAPTER 2 TEST, Cumulative Form

In 1-15, write each number as a decimal.

1. $10^4 \times .379$ 1. _____

2. 300 million   2. _____

3. $.001 \times 8.5$ 3. _____

4. 7 billionths   4. _____

5. 4.92×10^{-4} 5. _____

6. $\frac{5}{8}$ 6. _____

7. 8.08×10^7 7. _____

8. $6\frac{5}{3}$ 8. _____

9. $\frac{1}{100,000} \times 80$ 9. _____

10. thirty-two thousandths   10. _____

11. 10^8 11. _____

12. 10^0 12. _____

13. 8^3 13. _____

14. $\frac{4}{15}$ truncated to the ten-thousandth   14. _____

15. 10^{-5} 15. _____

16. What power of ten equals one thousandth?   16. _____

17. In 6^4, what is the 6 called?   17. _____

18. In 6^4, what is the 4 called?   18. _____

19. Which is larger: 6^4 or 4^6?   19. _____

20. Write a key sequence to enter 6^4 on your calculator.   20. _____

Name _____

In 21-26, complete the chart.

	Fraction		Decimal		Decimal
21.	?	**22.**	?		79%
	$\frac{7}{12}$	**23.**	?	**24.**	?
25.	?		1.63	**26.**	?

21. _____

22. _____

23. _____

24. _____

25. _____

26. _____

In 27 and 28, show your work.

27. What is 40% of 80?

27. _____

28. What is $\frac{3}{4}$% of 1000?

28. _____

29. Which letter corresponds to each position?

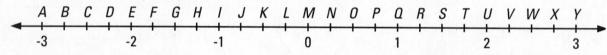

a. -1

b. 2.5

c. $-2\frac{1}{4}$

d. an integer that is neither positive nor negative

e. a point between $\frac{1}{5}$ and $\frac{2}{5}$

29. a. _____

b. _____

c. _____

d. _____

e. _____

30. A scale manufactured in Germany measures very small quantities to an accuracy of .00000000035 ounce. Write this number in scientific notation.

30. _____

31. You invest $1,000,000 in a certificate of deposit paying 5.25% a year. How much interest will you earn the first year?

31. _____

In 32 and 33, consider that the surface of the earth covers about 197 million square miles.

32. Write a key sequence to enter 197 million into your calculator.

32. _____

33. About 29.02% of the earth's surface is land. To the nearest million, estimate the number of square miles of land.

33. _____

In 34 and 35, use the circle graph below.

Kids' Favorite Fast Foods

McDonald's 43%

Other 27%

Burger King 10%

Taco Bell 13%

3% 4%

Pizza Hut

Wendy's

34. Find the categories that total half the circle.

34. _____

35. The survey involved 603 children. How many preferred Taco Bell?

35. _____

36. Give two reasons why it is an advantage to have several ways to write a number. You may want to use an example as part of your explanation.

_____

_____

_____

Now check all your work carefully.

QUIZ

In 1-5, fill in the blank with the correct number.

1. 1 mile = __?__ feet

2. __?__ cm = 1 in.

3. 1 cup = __?__ fluid ounces

4. 1 gallon = __?__ quarts

5. __?__ ounces = 1 pound

1. _____

2. _____

3. _____

4. _____

5. _____

Multiple choice. **In 6-9, pick the most sensible answer.**

6. A can of soda may contain

    (a) 12 ounces.   (b) 12 cups.

    (c) 12 pints.   (d) 12 quarts.

6. _____

7. The height of a 1-year-old child could be

    (a) 22 mm.   (b) 22 cm.

    (c) 22 in.   (d) 22 ft.

7. _____

8. The world record for the long jump is

    (a) 29.375 in.   (b) 29.375 cm.

    (c) 29.375 ft.   (d) 29.375 yd.

8. _____

9. A full-grown rhinoceros could weigh

    (a) 1000 ounces.   (b) 100 pounds.

    (c) 1000 grams.   (d) over one ton.

9. _____

10. Measure this segment to the indicated accuracy.

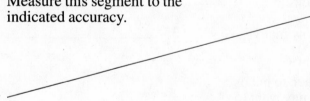

10. a. _____ $\frac{1}{2}$ in.

    b. _____ $\frac{1}{8}$ in.

    c. _____ cm

    d. _____ mm

11. Draw a 12.5-cm vertical line segment in the left margin.

12. Explain why it is important to have standardized units of measure.

_____

_____

_____

Name _____

QUIZ

In 1-6, fill in the blank with the correct number.

1. 1 kilogram = ___?___ grams

2. 1 milliliter = ___?___ liters

3. 1 meter = ___?___ centimeters

4. ___?___ pounds ≈ kilogram

5. ___?___ miles ≈ 1 kilometer

6. 1 liter ≈ ___?___ quarts

In 7-9, show the steps used to get your answer.

7. How many grams are in 4.5 kilograms?

8. Does a 2-liter bottle of soda hold more or less than a half gallon?

9. Standard distances in a short triathalon are a 1.5-km swim, a 40-km bike ride and a 10-km run. How far is each distance in miles?

In 10 and 11, draw a sketch for each description.

10. perpendicular lines

11. an obtuse angle *BAT*

In 12 and 13, measure each angle to the nearest degree.

12.   13.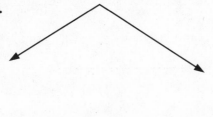

1. _____

2. _____

3. _____

4. _____

5. _____

6. _____

7. _____

8. _____

9. _____

10.

11.

12. _____

13. _____

CHAPTER 3 TEST, Form A

You will need a protractor and a ruler marked in inches and centimeters.

In 1-5, *multiple choice*. Give the letter of the correct answer.

1. The metric system was developed in which country?

    (a) Great Britain   (b) Germany

    (c) France   (d) the United States

    1. _____

2. In the three steps showing the conversion of 50 cm to meters, which step uses the Multiplication Property of Equality?

    (a) 1 cm = 0.01 m

    (b) 50 • 1 cm = 50 • 0.01 m

    (c) 50 cm = .50 m

    2. _____

3. The prefix *milli-* means

    (a) one thousandth.   (b) one thousand.

    (c) one millionth.   (d) one million.

    3. _____

4. A cubic foot contains

    (a) 12 cubic inches.   (b) 24 cubic inches.

    (c) 144 cubic inches.   (d) 1728 cubic inches.

    4. _____

5. The angle formed by a corner of this page is

    (a) an acute angle.   (b) a right angle.

    (c) an obtuse angle.   (d) perpendicular.

    5. _____

In 6-8, choose the most appropriate unit of measure.

6. a metric measure for the amount of juice in a juice box

    6. _____

7. a metric measure for the weight of a shot-put

    7. _____

8. a U.S. measure for the area of a sheet of poster board

    8. _____

In 9-12, fill in the blank.

9. 1 kilogram = __?__ grams

    9. _____

10. 8.6 kilometers = __?__ meters

    10. _____

11. __?__ fluid ounces = 1 cup

    11. _____

12. 1 ton = __?__ pounds

    12. _____

Name _____

In 13-17, use the figure at the right.

13. Measure $\overline{GA}$ to the nearest $\frac{1}{4}$ inch.

14. Measure $\overline{GE}$ to the nearest millimeter.

15. Measure $\angle E$.

16. List all acute angles in *GAME*.

17. List all obtuse angles in *GAME*.

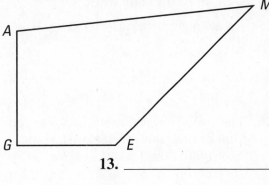

13. _____

14. _____

15. _____

16. _____

17. _____

18. Is a box that measures 2 feet on each side big enough to hold 9 cubic feet of sand?

18. _____

19. Draw and label an $\angle RED$ with measure 75°.

19.

20. Draw a horizontal line segment *GO* with length 4.8 cm.

20.

In 21-24, write ≈, <, >, or = to compare the two measures.

21. 10 inches ___?___ 25.4 cm

21. _____

22. 1 kg ___?___ 2.2 pounds

22. _____

23. 1 liter ___?___ 1 quart

23. _____

24. 1 square yard ___?___ 1 square meter

24. _____

In 25-28, show all your work.

25. An average car weighs 1500 kg. How many pounds is this?

25. _____

26. The 1992 Tour de France bicycle race took 21 days and covered 4016 km. How many miles is this?

26. _____

27. How many millimeters are in a kilometer?

27. _____

28. How many cup servings are in a half-gallon punch bowl?

28. _____

In 29 and 30, use this information: About 50% of the days of the year are school days, 20% are weekends during the school year, and 30% are vacations and holidays.

29. Complete the chart.

Days	Percent		Degrees	
School days	a.	?	b.	?
Weekends	c.	?	d.	?
Holidays	e.	?	f.	?

29. a. _____

b. _____

c. _____

d. _____

e. _____

f. _____

30. Draw a circle graph to represent the information.

30.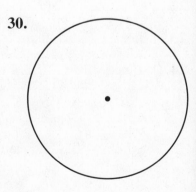

Now check all your work carefully.

CHAPTER 3 TEST, Form B

You will need a protractor and a ruler marked in inches and centimeters.

In 1-5, *multiple choice*. Give the letter of the correct answer.

1. The degree for measuring angles was developed by the

   (a) Babylonians.   (b) Germans.

   (c) Egyptians.   (d) Chinese.

   1. _____

2. In the three steps showing the conversion of 3 kg to grams, which step uses the Multiplication Property of Equality?

   (a) 1 kg = 1000 g

   (b) 3 • 1 kg = 3 • 1000 g

   (c) 3 kg = 3000 g

   2. _____

3. The prefix *kilo-* means

   (a) one thousandth.   (b) one thousand.

   (c) one millionth.   (d) one million.

   3. _____

4. A cubic yard contains

   (a) 27 cubic feet.   (b) 6 cubic feet.

   (c) 9 cubic feet.   (d) 144 cubic feet.

   4. _____

5. The angles formed by the wall and ceiling of a room are

   (a) acute angles.   (b) right angles.

   (c) obtuse angles.   (d) perpendicular.

   5. _____

In 6-8, choose the most appropriate unit of measure.

6. a metric measure for the amount of gasoline in a car's gas tank

   6. _____

7. a metric measure for the weight of a penny

   7. _____

8. a U.S. measure for the area of a book cover

   8. _____

In 9-12, fill in the blank.

9. 5 kilometers = ___?___ meters

   9. _____

10. 9.4 kilograms = ___?___ grams

   10. _____

11. ___?___ ounces = 1 pound

   11. _____

12. 1 gallon = ___?___ quarts

   12. _____

Name _____

In 13-17, use the figure at the right.

13. Measure $\overline{ZE}$ to the nearest $\frac{1}{4}$ inch.

14. Measure $\overline{ZA}$ to the nearest millimeter.

15. Measure $\angle B$.

16. List all acute angles in *ZEBRA*.

17. List all obtuse angles in *ZEBRA*.

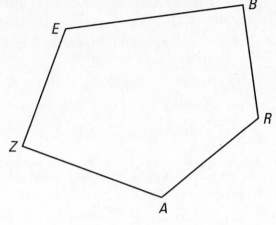

13. _____

14. _____

15. _____

16. _____

17. _____

18. Find the volume of a cube that measures 20 cm on each side.

18. _____

19. Draw and label an $\angle RED$ with measure 125°.

19.

20. Draw a horizontal line segment *RV* with length 5.2 cm.

20.

In 21-24, write $\approx$, $<$, $>$, or $=$ to compare the two measures.

21. 10 inches ___?___ 25 cm

21. _____

22. 1 kg ___?___ 1 pound

22. _____

23. 1 liter ___?___ 1.06 quarts

23. _____

24. 1 mi ___?___ 1 km

24. _____

In 25-28, show all your work.

25. A typical elevator capacity is 1250 kg. How many pounds is this?

25. _____

26. The length of the Nile River in Egypt is about 6700 km. How many miles is this?

26. _____

27. How many centimeters are in a kilometer?

27. _____

28. How many fluid ounces are in a half-gallon punch bowl?

28. _____

In 29 and 30, use this information. About 60% of the animals in a zoo are mammals, 30% are fish and birds, and 10% are reptiles.

29. Complete the chart.

Animals	Percent		Degrees	
Mammals	a.	?	b.	?
Fish and birds	c.	?	d.	?
Reptiles	e.	?	f.	?

29 a. _____

b. _____

c. _____

d. _____

e. _____

f. _____

30. Draw a circle graph to represent the information.

30.

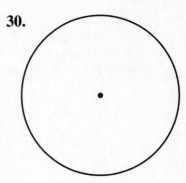

Now check all your work carefully .

CHAPTER 3 TEST, Form C

1. Use a ruler to draw a line segment that satisfies the following conditions:

To the nearest inch, its length is 3 in. To the nearest half inch, its length is $3\frac{1}{2}$ in.

Now find the length of your segment to the nearest *millimeter*.

2. You know that the area of a square is between 16 mm² and 36 mm². What do you know about the length of one side of this square?

This same square is one of the six faces of a cube. What do you know about the volume of the cube?

3. Your recipe for banana milkshakes requires 750 mL of milk. You want to triple the recipe, and you have a half gallon of milk in the refrigerator. Is this enough? Explain.

4. Without using a protractor, draw an obtuse angle. Label it ∠*RST*. Tell how you know that ∠*RST* is obtuse. Then use your protractor to find m∠*RST*.

5. Name something that you would measure in meters and something that you would measure in centimeters. Explain your reasoning.

If you had to measure the same things using the U.S. system of measurement, what units would you use?

6. The graph below shows the budget for the town of Midville. Explain how you know that it is drawn incorrectly. Then draw a corrected graph using the given percents.

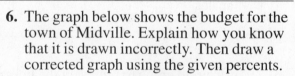
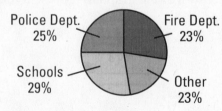

Police Dept. 25% Fire Dept. 23%

Schools 29% Other 23%

CHAPTER 3 TEST, Form D

You plan to start a business called *Cubic Aquariums*. The business will sell glass aquariums shaped like cubes. Several sizes of aquarium will be sold, ranging in capacity from at least one gallon to about nine or ten gallons. Each aquarium will be made from glass panels joined at their edges by metal strips, as shown in the sketch at the right. The top of the aquarium will be open.

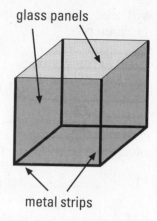

glass panels

metal strips

You need to accomplish these three tasks:

■ plan appropriate dimensions for the aquariums.
■ determine the amount of glass and metal needed to make the aquariums.
■ determine weights of the finished aquariums.

a. From an almanac, you learn that the volume of one gallon of water is 231 cubic inches. Suppose that the length of each edge of a cubic aquarium is 6 inches. Will it hold one gallon of water? Explain why or why not.

b. You want to start the business by offering just three different sizes of aquariums. Given the information above, what dimensions would you suggest for each of the three sizes? To the nearest tenth of a gallon, what is the capacity of each aquarium?

c. How much metal will be needed for each size of aquarium? How much glass?

d. You research the properties of the materials involved. The weights are given at the right. Use this information to find the weight of each aquarium you are suggesting when it is empty. What will be its weight when it is filled with water?

e. A friend of yours lives in Canada and wants to start a similar business. What metric measures would you suggest for the aquarium edges so that the Canadian versions are similar in size and shape to those you plan to manufacture? Explain why you chose those measures.

Water
8.3 pounds per gallon

Glass Panels
0.4 ounce per square inch

Metal Strips
0.2 ounce per inch

CHAPTER 3 TEST, Cumulative Form

You will need a protractor and a ruler marked in inches and centimeters.

In 1-6, fill in the blank.

1. _____?_____ feet = 1 mile

2. 1 inch = _____?_____ cm

3. 1 ton = _____?_____ pounds

4. 1 L = _____?_____ mL

5. 1 kg ≈ _____?_____ pounds

6. _____?_____ mm = 1 m

1. _____

2. _____

3. _____

4. _____

5. _____

6. _____

In 7-9, give an appropriate unit of measure for each quantity.

7. a metric measure for the weight of five grains of salt

8. a U.S. measure for the capacity of a small thermos

9. a metric measure for the height of a chair

7. _____

8. _____

9. _____

In 10-13, show your work in converting each measure.

10. How many liters are in 2342 mL?

10. _____

11. How many pints are in $1\frac{1}{2}$ gallons?

11. _____

12. It is 1660 km from Calcutta to Bombay, India. How far is this in miles?

12. _____

Name

13. The ceiling in Marla's room is 114 inches high. How high is this in feet and inches?

13. _____

14. **a.** Draw a line perpendicular to the line at the right.

14. a.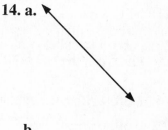

   b. What type of angle is formed?

   b. _____

15. **a.** Draw a square with side length 1.5 cm.

15. a.

   b. What is the area of the square?

   b. _____

16. Measure this segment

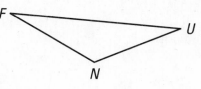

   a. to the nearest millimeter.

16. a. _____

   b. to the nearest $\frac{1}{8}$ in.

   b. _____

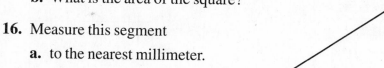

17. Use the triangle *FUN*.

   a. Find m∠*F*.

17. a. _____

   b. Name an obtuse angle.

   b. _____

▶ **CHAPTER 3 TEST,** **Cumulative Form** *page 3*

In 18-21, put $>$, $<$, $=$, or $\approx$ to make the sentence true.

18. $\frac{1}{2}$ gallon _____?_____ 2 quarts

18. _____

19. 1 pound _____?_____ 1 kg

19. _____

20. 1000 yd _____?_____ 1 km

20. _____

21. 5 liters _____?_____ 5.3 quarts

21. _____

22. A box is a cube with one edge measuring 8 inches. How much can the box hold?

22. _____

In 23-30, write each expression as a single decimal.

23. 3 billion

23. _____

24. 7 ten-thousandths

24. _____

25. $\frac{5}{6}$

25. _____

26. 725%

26. _____

27. 10^{-7}

27. _____

28. $5\frac{5}{8}$

28. _____

29. 4.2×10^5

29. _____

30. $.0001 \times 50$

30. _____

In 31-32, show your work.

31. William Clinton received 43.24% of the vote in the 1992 Presidential election.

a. What percent of voters did not vote for President Clinton?

31. a. _____

b. If about 101 million people voted, how many voted for Clinton? Round your answer to the nearest million.

b. _____

32. Write a fraction

   a. equal to $\frac{2}{3}$, with denominator 9.   **32. a.** _____

   b. equal to $\frac{78}{24}$, in lowest terms.   **b.** _____

   c. equal to 5, with denominator 4.   **c.** _____

   d. equal to $.\overline{3}$.   **d.** _____

   e. equal to 40%, in lowest terms.   **e.** _____

33. According to the *World Almanac,* in the fall of 1990, total enrollment in elementary and secondary day schools in the United States was 41,223,804.

   a. Round this number up to the next million.   **33. a.** _____

   b. Round this number down to the next million.   **b.** _____

   c. Round this number to the nearest million.   **c.** _____

   d. Write your answer to Part c in scientific notation.   **d.** _____

   e. Write your answer to Part c as a decimal followed by a word.   **e.** _____

Now check all your work carefully.

Name _____

COMPREHENSIVE TEST, Chapters 1-3

You will need a protractor and a ruler marked in inches
and centimeters.

In 1-25, *multiple choice*. Give the letter of the correct answer.

1. Four thousandths equals   1. _____

    (a) 4,000.   (b) .4000.

    (c) .004.   (d) .0004.

2. A store has grapes selling for $1.39 a pound. To find the cost of half   2. _____
   a pound, you calculate 1.39 ÷ 2 = .695. How much will you pay?

    (a) $.69   (b) .69 cents

    (c) $.70   (d) .70 cents

3. Two thirds as a decimal rounded to the nearest hundredth is   3. _____

    (a) .23.   (b) .66.

    (c) .666.   (d) .67.

4. Which key sequence will *not* evaluate 23^2?   4. _____

    (a) 23 $\boxed{\times}$ 2 $\boxed{=}$ (b) 23 $\boxed{x^2}$

    (c) 23 $\boxed{\times}$ 23 $\boxed{=}$ (d) 23 $\boxed{y^x}$ 2 $\boxed{=}$

5. Which number is *not* equal to the other three?   5. _____

    (a) $\frac{3}{11}$ (b) .27

    (c) $.\overline{27}$ (d) $.2\overline{72}$

6. "A depth of 50 feet below sea level is higher than 100 feet below   6. _____
   sea level" can be written

    (a) 50 > 100.   (b) 100 > 50.

    (c) -50 > -100.   (d) -50 < -100

7. Which number is graphed on the number line?   7. _____

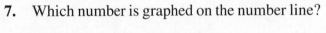

    (a) $2\frac{1}{4}$ (b) -1.75

    (c) -2.25   (d) -2.4

8. Tell which symbol makes this statement true: $\frac{2}{3}$ ___?___ $\frac{3}{4}$ 8. _____

    (a) >   (b) <

    (c) =   (d) ≈

9. $\frac{15}{45} = $ ___?___

9. _____

   (a) 3   (b) $\frac{1}{5}$

   (c) $\frac{1}{3}$ (d) $\frac{5}{9}$

10. The largest lottery prize, \$118.8 million (split by 10 winners, California, 1991), was

10. _____

   (a) \$118,000,000.   (b) \$118,800.

   (c) \$118,800,000,000.   (d) \$118,800,000.

11. $5^4 = $ ___?___

11. _____

   (a) 20   (b) 9

   (c) 625   (d) 125

12. Which number is written in scientific notation?

12. _____

   (a) 32×10^4 (b) 3.2×10^4

   (c) 3.2×8^3 (d) $3.2 \times 10^{3.5}$

13. $4.75\% = $ ___?___

13. _____

   (a) $\frac{475}{100}$ (b) 475

   (c) .0475   (d) 4.75

14. 75% of 40 = ___?___

14. _____

   (a) 30   (b) 3

   (c) .0475   (d) 4.75

15. As a fraction in lowest terms, 80% = ___?___.

15. _____

   (a) $\frac{80}{100}$ (b) $\frac{8}{10}$

   (c) $\frac{4}{5}$ (d) .8

16. Which number does *not* represent one thousandth?

16. _____

   (a) $\frac{1}{1000}$ (b) 10^{-2}

   (c) .001   (d) .1%

17. $.72 \times 10^{-5} = $ ___?___

17. _____

   (a) .000072   (b) .0000072

   (c) 720,000   (d) 7,200,000

18. The length of your calculator would most likely be measured in

18. _____

   (a) millimeters.   (b) centimeters.

   (c) meters.   (d) kilometers.

Name _____

19. A quarter mile equals

    (a) 440 feet.   (b) 880 feet.

    (c) 1320 feet.   (d) 1760 feet.

19. _____

20. The largest known meteorite was found in 1920 in Namibia. It is estimated to weigh 65 tons. This is about

    (a) 130 pounds.   (b) 1300 pounds.

    (c) 13,000 pounds.   (d) 130,000 pounds.

20. _____

21. 35 km = ___?___

    (a) 35,000 m   (b) 3500 m

    (c) 350 m   (d) .3500 m

21. _____

22. Which is largest?

    (a) pint   (b) liter

    (c) cup   (d) quart

22. _____

23. At 5:00, the hour hand and minute hand of a clock form

    (a) an acute angle.   (b) a right angle.

    (c) an obtuse angle.   (d) perpendicular lines.

23. _____

24. A square has a side measuring 15 cm. Its area is

    (a) 30 cm².   (b) 60 cm².

    (c) 225 cm.   (d) 225 cm².

24. _____

25. The volume of a cube with edge 4 inches is

    (a) 16 in.²   (b) 64 in.²

    (c) 16 in.³   (d) 64 in.³

25. _____

26. In 1991, the U.S. minted 13,135,307,239 coins (pennies, nickels, and so on). Round this number

    a. to the nearest 1000.

    b. to the nearest million.

    c. up to the next million.

    d. to the nearest billion.

26. a. _____

b. _____

c. _____

d. _____

27. Change $\frac{7}{12}$ to a decimal.

    a. What is a calculator key sequence?

    b. Write the calculator display.

27. a. _____

b. _____

Name _____

28. Graph each number on the number line below: $\frac{1}{2}$, 3.75, -4, -2.25, -.5

28.

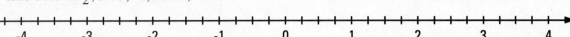

29. Write each number in scientific notation.

   a. personal savings in U.S. in 1991 of $219.3 billion

   b. lowest temperature reached on the Kelvin Scale: 0.000000002° Kelvin

29. a. _____

   b. _____

30. Estimate the percent represented by each sector of this circle graph.

   a. sector A

   b. sector B

   c. sector C

30. a. _____

   b. _____

   c. _____

In 31-33, show your work.

31. A tip in a restaurant is often 15% of the cost of the meal. If your bill is $6.79, what will be your total cost, including tip?

31. _____

32. How many pints are in a gallon?

32. _____

33. How many centimeters are in a yard?

33. _____

34. Find each measure in triangle *TRY*.

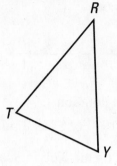

   a. *TR* to the nearest millimeter

   b. *RY* to the nearest $\frac{1}{8}$ inch

   c. m∠*Y*

34. a. _____

   b. _____

   c. _____

35. Evaluate and write the answer in scientific notation:
369,000,000 ÷ .000006.

35. _____

36. Do you think the U.S. should adopt the metric system?
Explain why or why not.

_____

_____

_____

_____

_____

Now check all your work carefully.

QUIZ

In 1 and 2, evaluate each expression.

1. $10r - m^2$, when $r = 4.3$ and $m = 4$

    1. _____

2. $16 - 3 + 2^2 \cdot 5 \div 5$

    2. _____

In 3-6, translate into algebra.

3. 6 less than a number

    3. _____

4. 6 is less than a number.

    4. _____

5. 6 less a number

    5. _____

6. There are c children in the room. How many will there be if 7 more children enter and y children leave?

    6. _____

7. Three instances of a general pattern are given. Describe the pattern using one variable.

    $(2)^4 = 2 \times 2 \times 2 \times 2$

    $(1.2)^4 = 1.2 \times 1.2 \times 1.2 \times 1.2$

    $\left(\frac{1}{2}\right)^4 = \frac{1}{2} \times \frac{1}{2} \times \frac{1}{2} \times \frac{1}{2}$

    7. _____

8. Give an instance of this pattern:

    $\ell + \ell + w + w = 2\ell + 2w$

    8. _____

9. In your pocket are $.25q + .10d + .05n + .01p$ dollars, where q is the number of quarters, d is the number of dimes, n is the number of nickels, and p is the number of pennies. What is the total if you have 5 quarters, 3 nickels, 2 pennies, and 6 dimes?

    9. _____

10. Felicita earns money by doing the activities listed.

Activity	Earnings per Hour
Mowing lawns	$5
Washing windows	$6.50
Babysitting	$3.50

    a. What will Felicita earn for washing windows for four hours and babysitting for 3 hours?

    10. a. _____

    b. How much more will she earn by washing windows for two hours than by babysitting for three hours?

    b. _____

QUIZ

In 1-4, evaluate each expression.

1. $\dfrac{15 + 8}{9 + 1}$

2. $\dfrac{20 + 28}{2^3}$

3. $38 - 3(8 - 5)^2$

4. $160 - [22 \div 11 + 3]$

5. Find the area of this rectangle in square inches.

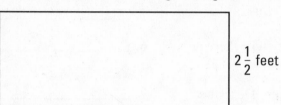

$2\frac{1}{2}$ feet

72 inches

6. Find the area of the shaded region between the two squares.

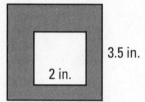

3.5 in.

2 in.

7. Evaluate $2l + 2w$ when $l = 9.2$ and $w = 6$.

8. Ian has scored 91, 68, and 86 points on consecutive chapter tests. Each test has a possible 100 points. What is the highest possible average Ian could have after the next test?

9. You tossed a fair die 150 times with these results.

Six was tossed 23 times.   Five was tossed 30 times.
Four was tossed 19 times.   Three was tossed 40 times.
Two was tossed 13 times.   One was tossed 25 times.

What was the relative frequency that an even number was tossed?

1. _____

2. _____

3. _____

4. _____

5. _____

6. _____

7. _____

8. _____

9. _____

Name _____

CHAPTER 4 TEST, Form A

1. *Multiple choice.* Of what nationality was the person who first used letters of the alphabet to describe patterns?

   (a) Arabic   (b) French

   (c) Greek   (d) Italian

   1. _____

2. In $3(x + 2) = 3x + 6$, what is x called?

   2. _____

3. Use one variable to describe the pattern for these instances.

   One folder has $1 \cdot 2$ pockets.

   Two folders have $2 \cdot 2$ pockets.

   Three folders have $3 \cdot 2$ pockets.

   3. _____

4. Three instances of a pattern are given. Describe the pattern using two variables.

   $\frac{1}{7} \times \frac{8}{9} = \frac{8}{9} \times \frac{1}{7}$

   $5 \times 4 = 4 \times 5$

   $-2 \times 3.5 = 3.5 \times -2$

   4. _____

5. Give two instances of this pattern:

   $n + 0 = n$

   5. _____

   _____

In 6-10, translate into algebra. Let n stand for the number.

6. the product of seven and a number divided by the sum of seven and the number

   6. _____

7. twice the number, plus 10

   7. _____

8. Negative twelve is less than the number.

   8. _____

9. nine less a number

   9. _____

10. nine less than a number

   10. _____

11. *Multiple choice.* Written on one line, $\frac{15 + 3^2}{5 - 2}$ is

   (a) $(15 + 3^2)/(5 - 2)$.   (b) $15 + 3^2/(5 - 2)$.

   (c) $15 + 3^2/5 - 2$.   (d) $(15 + 3^2)/5 - 2$.

   11. _____

45 ▶

In 12-17, evaluate each expression.

12. $150 - 6(19 - 7)$

12. _____

13. $16 + 8 \cdot 3 - 12 \div 4$

13. _____

14. $16 \div \frac{8}{4} + 5$

14. _____

15. $(t + a)(2a - t)$ if $t = 9$ and $a = 16$

15. _____

16. $24 + 4m$, if $m = 3.5$

16. _____

17. $x + 6[x + 2(x - 2)]$, if $x = 2.5$

17. _____

18. *Multiple choice.* Which number is a solution to $2z + 1 = 5$?

    (a) 5   (b) 4

    (c) 3   (d) 2

18. _____

19. *Multiple choice.* Which number is *not* a solution to the inequality $2w < 7$?

    (a) -2   (b) 2

    (c) 3.5   (d) 0

19. _____

**In 20-23, find a solution to the sentence.
Show your work.**

20. $m - 8 = 12$

20. _____

21. t is a number less than -3.

21. _____

22. _____

22. $3w = 51$

23. $\frac{y}{6} = 9$

23. _____

24. The solutions to what sentence are graphed here?

24. _____

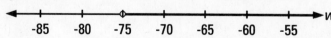

25. Graph all solutions to $-2.5 < t \le 0$.

25.

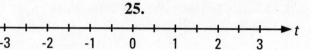

26. The formula $d = 16t^2$ can be used to estimate the number of feet d an object will fall in t seconds. Approximately how many feet will an object fall in 3 seconds?

26. _____

27. A formula for finding a baseball player's batting average is $A = \frac{H}{B}$, where A stands for *batting average*, H stands for *hits* and B for *at bats*. The number A is rounded to the nearest thousandth. In 1992, Gary Sheffield of the San Diego Padres had the highest batting average in the American League with 184 hits in 557 at bats. What was his batting average?

27. _____

28. Suppose you have 12 coins in your pocket, and 5 of these coins are pennies. If you take a coin out of your pocket at random, what is the probability that the coin you pick

a. will be a penny?

28. a. _____

b. will *not* be a penny?

b. _____

29. Suppose you roll a six-sided die 100 times and it lands with 3 showing 50 times. Should you believe the die is fair? Why or why not?

_____

_____

_____

_____

_____

Now check all your work carefully.

CHAPTER 4 TEST, Form B

1. *Multiple choice.* Who is sometimes called the "father of algebra"?

    (a) Léonard Euler   (b) Jacques Bernoulli

    (c) Ross Perot   (d) Francois Viéte

    1. _____

2. What is the difference between a *pattern* and an *instance*?

    _____

    _____

3. Use one variable to describe the pattern for these instances.

    One watch has 1 • 3 hands.

    Three watches have 3 • 3 hands.

    Five watches have 5 • 3 hands.

    3. _____

4. Three instances of a pattern are given. Describe the pattern using two variables.

    -(4 − 3) = 3 − 4

    -(6 − .5) = .5 − 6

    -(80% − 70%) = 70% − 80%

    4. _____

5. Give two instances of this pattern:

    $t + t = 2t$

    5. _____

    _____

In 6-10, translate into algebra. Let *n* stand for the number.

6. the quotient of 12 and the product of three and the number

    6. _____

7. half the number, decreased by seven

    7. _____

8. Negative two is greater than the number.

    8. _____

9. fifteen less a number

    9. _____

10. fifteen less than a number

    10. _____

11. *Multiple choice.* Written on one line, $\dfrac{2 \cdot 4 + 6}{5 - 3}$ is

    (a) $(2 \cdot 4 + 6)/5 - 3$.   (b) $2(4 + 6)/(5 - 3)$.

    (c) $(2 \cdot 4 + 6)/(5 - 3)$.   (d) $2 \cdot 4 + 6/(5 - 3)$.

    11. _____

In 12-17, evaluate each expression.

12. $20 + 6 \cdot 4 - 15 \div 3$

12. _____

13. $200 - 5(16 - 4)$

13. _____

14. $75 \div \frac{25}{5} + 8$

14. _____

15. $(2y + 3)(2y - x)$ if $y = 7$ and $x = 5$

15. _____

16. $32 + 3m$, if $m = 1.5$

16. _____

17. $t + 4[t + 3(t - 2)]$, if $t = 2.5$

17. _____

18. *Multiple choice.* Which number is a solution to $\frac{1}{2}x + 3 = 7$?

18. _____

   (a) 2   (b) 4

   (c) 8   (d) 10

19. *Multiple choice.* Which number is *not* a solution to the inequality $4y < 10$?

19. _____

   (a) 0   (b) -2

   (c) 2   (d) 2.5

**In 20-23, find a solution to the sentence.
Show your work.**

20. $m - 16 = 22$

20. _____

21. t is a number less than -1.

21. _____

22. $4w = 96$

22. _____

23. $\frac{y}{6} = 7$

23. _____

24. The solutions to what sentence are graphed here?

24. _____

25. Graph all solutions to $-2.5 \leq t \leq -1$.

    25.

26. A formula to calculate the area A of a circle is $A = \pi r^2$ where r is the radius. What is the area of a circle with a radius of 6 feet?

    26. _____

27. The formula for finding a team's winning percent P in many sporting events is $P = 100\left(\frac{W}{W+L}\right)$, where W stands for the number of *wins* and L stands for the number of *losses*. The number P is rounded to the nearest thousandth. In the 1992-93 NBA season, the Phoenix Suns had the highest win-loss record. The Suns ended with 75 wins and 31 losses including playoffs. What was their winning percent?

    27. _____

28. Julie picked a numbered ticket out of a hat. There were 35 tickets in the hat numbered 1 through 35. What is the probability that Julie's ticket had an even number on it?

    28. _____

29. Write a paragraph explaining what a probability of 1 means *and* why a probability can never be more than 1.

    _____

    _____

    _____

    _____

    _____

Now check all your work carefully.

CHAPTER 4 TEST, Form C

1. Use each of the numbers and symbols in the box below exactly once. Create a numerical expression whose value is greater than 10 and less than 20. What is the value of your expression?

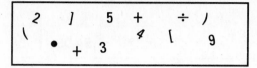

2. The figure shown below is a rectangle. The formula $A = \ell w$ gives its area in terms of length and width. Sketch a rectangle that has the same area but a different length and width. Label the length and width.

3 yd

4 ft

3. Identify a real-world pattern that could be described by the variable expression $4n$. Give three instances of the pattern.

4. Explain the difference between evaluating the algebraic expression $14 - y$ and solving the equation $14 - y = 5$.

5. Refer to the spinner at the right. Name two different events related to the spinner whose probability is $\frac{1}{3}$.

Explain your reasoning.

6. Name a number graphed on line m that is not graphed on line n. Then name a number graphed on line n that is not graphed on line m.

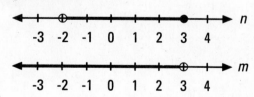

CHAPTER 4 TEST, Form D

You work in the school bookstore and are assigned to keep track of the items that are imprinted with your school name. Your school buys each item at a wholesale price (W) and sells it at a retail price (R). You compute the school's profit (P) using the formula $P = R - W$.

The chart at the right gives the wholesale and retail prices for each school-imprint item that is sold in the bookstore.

School-Imprint Items			
	Wholesale Price	**Retail Price**	**Profit**
Clothing			
T-shirts	$3.39	$4.99	
sweatshirts	$5.39	$7.99	
jackets	$16.69	$24.99	
caps	$3.99	$5.99	
Supplies			
notebooks	79¢	$1.39	
3-ring binders	$2.19	$3.79	
pencils	39¢	69¢	
ball-point pens	69¢	$1.19	
decals	39¢	69¢	

a. Use the formula given above to complete the *Profit* column of the table.

b. What is the total amount of profit if you sell two T-shirts? three? four? Describe the pattern using variables.

c. Suppose that you want to make a profit of exactly $8 from the sale of T-shirts. Write an equation that you can solve to find the number of T-shirts you need to sell. What is the solution to your equation? How many T-shirts must you sell?

d. Suppose that you want to make a profit of *at least* $20 from the sale of T-shirts. What is the least number of T-shirts you must sell? Explain your answer.

e. The principal has decided that the profits from the sale of all school-imprint items during the month of October will be donated to the town scholarship fund. The goal is to donate a total of $1000. Your task is to estimate the number of each item that must be sold in order to meet this goal. Write a memo to the principal that presents your estimates and any expressions, equations, and calculations you used to arrive at them. Include a graph that can be enlarged and placed on a poster to display your estimates in the school bookstore.

CHAPTER 4 TEST, Cumulative Form

1. In $5 + 3 \times 2^2$, which operation should you do first?

1. _____

2. Give an instance of the pattern $3b + b = 4b$.

2. _____

3. Write an algebraic expression for "a number divided by 10."

3. _____

4. Write $\frac{x + y}{x - y}$ on one line.

4. _____

5. Write a formula for finding p when p is 25% of b.

5. _____

6. There are ten boys and twelve girls at the rollerskating rink. If a random skater is picked for a free pass to the rink, what is the probability the pass will be received by a girl?

6. _____

7. The weather forecast for Saturday includes a 40% chance of rain. What is the probability that it will *not* rain?

7. _____

8. Find r, when $3r = 36$.

8. _____

9. *Multiple choice.* What is the solution to $5 + 2j = 14$?

(a) 2   (b) 14   (c) 4.5   (d) 0

9. _____

10. Give one solution to $-4 < s < -1.5$.

10. _____

In 11 and 12, graph all solutions.

11. $m > 3.5$

11.

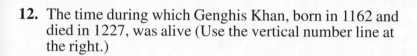

m

12. The time during which Genghis Khan, born in 1162 and died in 1227, was alive (Use the vertical number line at the right.)

12.

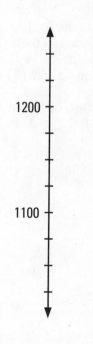

1200

1100

Name _____

In 13-15, evaluate the expression. Show your work.

13. $20.5 + 3.5^2 - 10$ 13. _____

14. $\dfrac{20 - 2^3}{5 - 2}$ 14. _____

15. $50 - 3t^2$, when $t = 4$ 15. _____

16. Three instances of a pattern are given. Use two variables   16. _____
to write the general pattern.

$$8 \cdot 3 + 8 \cdot 4 = 8\,(3 + 4)$$

$$8 \cdot \tfrac{1}{2} + 8 \cdot \tfrac{2}{3} = 8\,(\tfrac{1}{2} + \tfrac{2}{3})$$

$$8 \cdot 3.2 + 8 \cdot 4.5 = 8\,(3.2 + 4.5)$$

17. Tickets for a concert cost $10, $15, or $20. If t tickets   17. _____
were sold for $10, f for $15, and w for $20, what
expression represents the total ticket revenue?

18. In baseball, a person's batting average is figured by $\dfrac{H}{AB}$.   18. _____
H stands for hits and AB for times at bat. This number is
rounded to the nearest thousandth. Find Edgar
Martinez's 1992 average, highest in the major leagues,
when he had 181 hits in 528 at bats.

19. Write a different sentence with the same solutions   19. _____
as $-6 \le q < -3$.

20. Explain the difference between *probability* and
relative frequency.

_____

_____

_____

In 21-22, fill in the blank.

21. ___?___ inches = 1 yard   **21.** _____

22. 500 g = ___?___ kg   **22.** _____

23. What metric unit would you use to measure the amount   **23.** _____
of salt in a serving of cereal?

24. Write the name for the   **24.** _____
figure at the right.

25. Find the area of a square with side $\frac{1}{2}$ inch.   **25.** _____

26. Write the decimal for $5.5 billion, the amount   **26.** _____
Texaco paid Pennzoil in 1987 for damages due to
unethical tactics.

27. Write .0000000003 m, the diameter of some atoms, in   **27.** _____
scientific notation.

28. Write 60% as a fraction in lowest form.   **28.** _____

29. The area of Nepal is about 56,136 square miles. Round   **29.** _____
this number down to the preceding thousand.

30. Which is larger: $\frac{11}{12}$ or $\frac{23}{25}$?   **30.** _____

31. To the nearest foot, how many feet are in a kilometer?   **31.** _____

32. Convert 100 inches to feet and inches.   **32.** _____

33. In the circle at the right, make sector *A* 25%, sector *B* 40%, and sector *C* 35% of the circle.

33.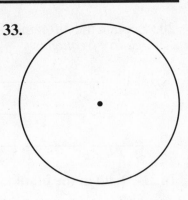

34. Write two key sequences for entering 3.6×10^8 in your calculator.

34. _____

_____

35. Put in order from smallest to largest:

$-\frac{3}{5}$ 45% 6.3×10^{-3} -2

35. _____

36. Write 2.7

    a. as a mixed number.

36. a. _____

    b. as a simple fraction.

        b. _____

    c. as a percent.

        c. _____

    d. rounded to the nearest integer.

        d. _____

QUIZ

In 1-5, simplify. Do *not* use a calculator.

1. -21.2 + -8.9

                                                  1. _____

2. 15 + -20

    2. _____

3. -4.5 + 3

    3. _____

4. $|-8| + |9|$

    4. _____

5. $|-8 + 9|$

    5. _____

6. If $x = -3$, then $-(-x) = $ ___?___ .

    6. _____

7. If $a = 4$ and $b = -5$, then $a + -b = $ ___?___ .

    7. _____

8. Draw a picture of -6 + 8 using a number line and arrows.

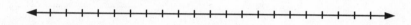

9. How many degrees is a quarter turn?

    9. _____

10. All central angles pictured have equal measure. What is the magnitude of the turn pictured by the arrow?

    10. _____

11. **a.** What number is called the additive identity?

    11. a. _____

    b. Why?

_____

_____

12. What is another name for additive inverse?

    12. _____

13. This week Molly earned $15, spent $7.25, earned $9.50, and then spent $6.75.

    a. Write an addition problem that shows Molly's financial activity.

    13. a. _____

    b. How much did Molly still have from this week's earnings?

    b. _____

14. Identify the property illustrated in each example.

    a. 100.4 + 0 = 100.4

    14. a. _____

    b. -671 + 671 = 0

    b. _____

QUIZ

1. Match each equation with the property or properties it illustrates.

   i. Commutative Property of Addition   ii. Associative Property of Addition
  iii. both properties   iv. neither property

   a. $(3 \cdot 4) \cdot 5 = 3 \cdot (4 \cdot 5)$ **1. a.** _____

   b. $(\frac{1}{2} + \frac{1}{4}) + -\frac{1}{4} = \frac{1}{2} + (\frac{1}{4} + -\frac{1}{4})$ **b.** _____

   c. $7(2 + 8) = 7(8 + 2)$ **c.** _____

   d. $8 + (9 + 10) = (9 + 8) + 10$ **d.** _____

In 2 and 3, simplify. Give answers in lowest terms.

2. $-2\frac{1}{6} + 1\frac{5}{6}$ **2.** _____

3. $-\frac{2}{3} + \frac{4}{5} + -\frac{3}{10}$ **3.** _____

In 4 and 5, solve each equation. Show your work.

4. $a + -2.3 = 5.1$ **4.** _____

5. $5\frac{3}{4} = 1\frac{1}{8} + c$ **5.** _____

In 6 and 7, solve each problem.

6. You have 2 white shirts, 3 blue shirts, 1 tan shirt, and 1 shirt that is plaid. If it is dark and you cannot see which shirt you are choosing, what is the probability it will be white or tan?

           6. _____
                      calculation

                      _____
                        answer

7. Lareta needs a total of 360 points on four tests to get an A in math this semester. If she has 93, 82, and 91 on her first three tests, what is the minimum score she needs to earn an A?

           7. _____
                      calculation

                      _____
                        answer

CHAPTER 5 TEST, Form A

In 1-8, simplify.

1. $4 + -8.9$

2. $|-9 + 5|$

3. $-(8 + -10)$

4. $-12.5 + -8 + 4$

5. $-|9| + |-10.5|$

6. $-(-(0 + -3.5))$

7. $\dfrac{-6}{a} + \dfrac{5}{a}$

8. $\dfrac{1}{3} + \dfrac{3}{4}$

1. _____

2. _____

3. _____

4. _____

5. _____

6. _____

7. _____

8. _____

9. *Multiple choice.* Which property is illustrated by $(\frac{1}{2} + 7) + -\frac{1}{2} = -\frac{1}{2} + (\frac{1}{2} + 7)$?

9. _____

    (a) Property of Opposites

    (b) Commutative Property of Addition

    (c) Associative Property of Addition

10. Give an instance of the Additive Identity Property of Zero.

10. _____

11. These are 3 possible events when a six-sided die is rolled:

11. _____

    A: an even number is showing.

    B: 1, 2, or 3 is showing.

    C: 4, 5, or 6 is showing.

    Which two of the events are mutually exclusive?

12. There are 4 pairs of white socks in your drawer, 5 pairs of blue, 3 pairs of black and one pair of brown. What is the probability that you will reach for a pair in the dark and pull out a blue or black pair?

12. _____

13. Suppose the probability you have an English test tomorrow is 25% and the probability you have a science test tomorrow is 30%. Explain why the probability that you will have one of these tests is *not* 55%.

_____

_____

_____

14. Is this number positive, negative, or zero?

14. _____

    468.1121314115 + -468.1121314151

In 15-18, solve and check. Show your work.

15. $-15 = s + 4$ 16. $-9 + r + 6 = 1\frac{1}{2}$

15. _____

16. _____

17. _____

17. $12 = d + -0.8$ 18. $-\frac{1}{6} + f = 1$

18. _____

In 19 and 20, assume all small angles with vertex _O_ have the same measure.

19. What is the magnitude of the counterclockwise turn from _C_ to _F_ around point _O_?

19. _____

20. If you stand at point _O_ facing _B_, what is the magnitude of the clockwise turn you must make to face _A_?

20. _____

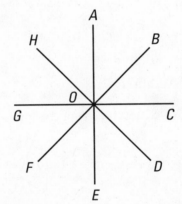

For 21 and 22, use the diagram below.

_S_   _A_   _K_

21. What equation relates _AS, SK,_ and _AK_?

21. _____

22. If _SK_ = 9.5 cm and _KA_ = 7 cm, find _AS_.

22. _____

23. **a.** Use arrows to picture -3 + 8 on the number line.

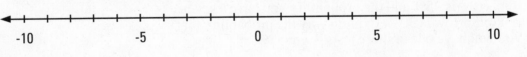

    b. Give the sum.

23. **b.** _____

24. A rectangular skating rink is *d* meters longer than it is wide. If its width is 60 m, how long is the rink?

24. _____

25. Mr. Huynh took *B* boys, *G* girls, and *C* additional chaperones on a field trip. 31 people went altogether. How are *B, G, C,* and 31 related?

25. _____

26. Josie was behind 26 pages in her reading assignments. After reading last night, she is now 32 pages ahead of her class. Let *p* be the number of pages Josie read.

  a. What addition equation can be solved to find *p*?

26. a. _____

  b. Find *p*.

  b. _____

27. A heptagon has two sides of length 7 inches, two sides of length 3.2 inches and two sides of length 4.5 inches. The perimeter is 38 inches. Let *S* be the seventh side.

  a. What equation can be solved to find *S*?

27. a. _____

  b. Find *S*.

  b. _____

In 28-30, refer to the polygon pictured.

28. What is a name for this particular polygon?

28. _____

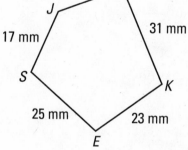

29. How many vertices does the polygon have?

29. _____

30. Calculate its perimeter.

30. _____

31. Write an explanation of how you would teach a younger sister to add one positive and one negative number together.

_____

_____

_____

_____

Now check all your work carefully.

CHAPTER 5 TEST, Form B

In 1-8, simplify.

1. -7 + 4.6

2. |3 + -16|

3. -(13 + -29)

4. -11 + -14.5 + 8

5. -|6| + |-12.5|

6. -(-(8.1 + 0))

7. $\dfrac{-9}{a} + \dfrac{3}{a}$

8. $\dfrac{2}{3} + \dfrac{3}{5}$

9. *Multiple choice.* Which property is illustrated by
   $8 + \left(-\dfrac{3}{4} + 5\right) = 8 + \left(5 + -\dfrac{3}{4}\right)$?

   (a) Property of Opposites

   (b) Commutative Property of Addition

   (c) Associative Property of Addition

10. *Multiple choice.* Which property is
    illustrated by -33 + 33 = 0?

    (a) Additive Identity Property of Zero

    (b) Opposite of Opposites Property

    (c) Property of Opposites

11. Here are 3 possible events that might
    occur on your report card.

    A: You get an A in Math.

    B: You get a B in English.

    C: You get a B in Math.

    Which two of these events are mutually exclusive?

12. An aquarium has 3 angelfish, 2 catfish, 12 guppies, and
    15 swordfish in it. If you select one of these fish without
    looking, what is the probability that it will *not* be a guppy?

13. Suppose the probability of your having pasta salad for dinner tonight
    is 15% and the probability of your having chicken soup is 35%. Explain
    why the probability that you will have one of these is *not* 50%.

    _____

    _____

1. _____

2. _____

3. _____

4. _____

5. _____

6. _____

7. _____

8. _____

9. _____

10. _____

11. _____

12. _____

14. Is this number positive, negative, or zero?

14. _____

305.2245673244 + -305.2245672344

In 15-18, solve and check. Show your work.

15. $16 = y + -1.6$ **16.** $-14 = t + 8$

15. _____

16. _____

17. _____

17. $17 + r + -25 = 3\frac{1}{2}$ **18.** $m + -\frac{3}{8} = 2$

18. _____

In 19 and 20, refer to this picture of a standard clock.

19. What is the measure of the angle formed by the hands of the clock at 11:00?

19. _____

20. What is the magnitude of the turn that the *minute* hand makes from 11:00 to 11:25?

20. _____

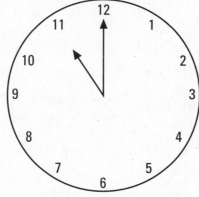

For 21 and 22, use the diagram below.

P   *R*   *Q*

21. What equation relates *RQ, PQ,* and *PR*?

21. _____

22. If *PR* = 3.2 cm and *PQ* = 13 cm, find *PR*.

22. _____

23. a. Use arrows to picture 6 + -8 on the number line.

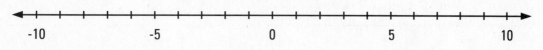

-10   -5   0   5   10

b. Give the sum.

23. b. _____

24. A bedroom is t meters longer than it is wide. If its width is 5 m, how long is the room?

24. _____

25. Suppose you are the first person to get on the bus. Three minutes later P more passengers get on and five minutes after that, Q more passengers get on to make a total of 47 passengers on the bus. How are P, Q, and 47 related?

25. _____

26. The Lancer volleyball team was losing by 7 points but is now winning by 3. Let p be the change in points.

    a. What equation can be solved to find p?

26. a. _____

    b. Find p.

    b. _____

27. A pentagon has two sides of length 2.5 cm, one side of length 9 cm, and one side of length 7.5 cm. The perimeter is 28 cm. Let S be the fifth side.

    a. What equation can be solved to find S?

27. a. _____

    b. Find S.

    b. _____

In 28-30, refer to the polygon pictured.

28. What is a name of this particular polygon?

28. _____

29. Name a diagonal.

29. _____

30. Calculate the perimeter of the polygon.

30. _____

T 30 mm Y
12 mm   15 mm
              A
U
           20 mm
27 mm
              D
E
   25 mm   25 mm
        S

31. Write an explanation of how you would teach a younger sister to add two or three negative numbers together.

    _____

    _____

    _____

    _____

Now check all your work carefully.

CHAPTER 5 TEST, Form C

1. Draw a picture to show why the results of these two additions are different.

    $-5 + 7$ $5 + -7$

2. Write a problem that you can solve with the following equation. Then show how to use the equation to solve your problem.

    $$n + 5 = 4$$

3. Choose from the fractions in the box below. Find three numbers whose sum is

    a. positive.   **b.** negative.   **c.** zero.

    Find each sum.

$\frac{3}{4}$	$-\frac{5}{12}$	$\frac{1}{4}$	$\frac{1}{3}$	$-\frac{1}{3}$	$\frac{1}{12}$

4. Use a ruler marked in millimeters to draw a hexagon. Label its vertices and give its name. Then find its perimeter to the nearest millimeter.

5. Is the result of a 45° clockwise turn followed by a 135° counterclockwise turn the same as the result of a 135° counterclockwise turn followed by a 45° clockwise turn? What property of addition supports your answer?

6. Each of the 6 faces of a cube is to be labeled with one of the numbers 1, 2, 3, or 4. Tell how to label the faces so that

    a. the probability of rolling a 1 or 2 is $\frac{1}{3}$.

    b. the probability of *not* rolling a 3 is $\frac{2}{3}$.

CHAPTER 5 TEST, Form D

You are helping a friend build a new personal-use robot. So far, the robot responds to the commands shown in the chart at the right. To sketch the moves of the robot on paper, you use the symbol ⟳ to represent the robot. Each inch on paper represents one yard of actual movement. For instance, suppose the robot starts at its "home base" in the corner of the kitchen shown below. Then this set of commands takes it along the dashed-line path to the refrigerator.

$$\text{TURN } 45 \quad \text{MOVE } 2\frac{1}{16} \quad \text{TURN } -90 \quad \text{MOVE } 4\frac{5}{8} \quad \text{TURN } 45$$

a. Write a set of commands that will move the robot from its home base to face the sink. Then write a set of commands that will return the robot to its original position at home base.

b. What is the total distance that the robot travels in its round trip between home base and the sink?

c. Find several places in the kitchen to which the robot can move. For each location, write a set of commands that will move the robot there from its position at home base, and then return it to its original position. Calculate the distance the robot moves in that round trip. Organize your work so that your friend can read it easily and use it to program the robot.

TURN followed by a number of degrees	
If the number is	*the turn is*
positive	counter-clockwise
negative	clockwise
zero	no turn

MOVE followed by a number of yards	
If the number is	*the move is*
positive	forward
negative	backward
zero	no move

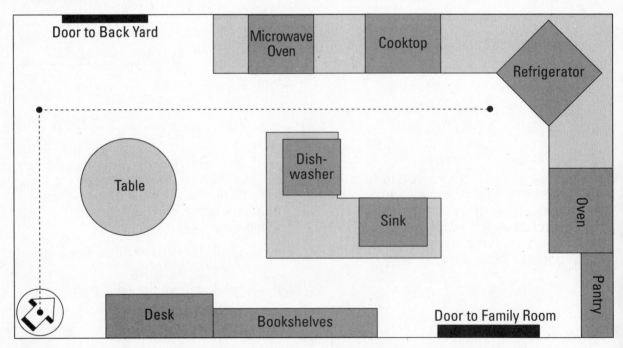

CHAPTER 5 TEST, Cumulative Form

1. Write 35 grams + 500 milligrams as one quantity.

   1. _____

2. The Property of Opposites states: For any number n, ___?___ .

   2. _____

3. Evaluate: $|-10|$

   3. _____

4. Write a calculator key sequence to evaluate $-3.25 + 4.08$.

   4. _____

5. In three days, how many degrees does the earth rotate on its axis?

   5. _____

6. Write $3\frac{2}{5}$ as a common fraction.

   6. _____

7. You roll a die. What is the probability that you will get a 1 or a number greater than 4?

   7. _____

8. Give an instance of the Associative Property of Addition.

   8. _____

9. *Multiple choice.* Which equation does *not* have the same solution as the others?

   9. _____

   (a) $x + -8 = 5$ (b) $-8 + x = 5$

   (c) $-8 = x + 5$ (d) $5 = x + -8$

10. What is the perimeter of a square with side 3 cm?

    10. _____

In 11-14, simplify. Give fraction answers in lowest terms.

11. $|-23| + -18 + -3.7$

    11. _____

12. $m + -n + p + n + -m$

    12. _____

13. $\frac{3}{n} + \frac{5}{n} + \frac{7}{n}$

    13. _____

14. $\frac{9}{10} + -\frac{3}{4}$

    14. _____

In 15 and 16, solve the equation. Show your work.

15. $y + -8 = -2$

15. _____

16. $4\frac{1}{3} = p + -2\frac{5}{6}$

16. _____

17. a. Use arrows to picture $5 + -7$ on the number line.

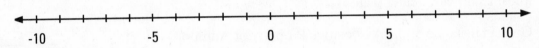

  b. Give the sum.

17. b. _____

18. Isabella is facing directly north. She turns $\frac{1}{2}$ a revolution clockwise, then $\frac{3}{8}$ a revolution counterclockwise. Draw a representation to show her turns and indicate in which direction she is facing.

18. _____

19. Is division commutative? Support your answer.

_____

_____

20. Evaluate $6 \cdot 4^2 - (10 \div 2)^2$.

20. _____

21. If $a = 3.5$, what does $(a + 2)(a - 3)$ equal?

21. _____

22. What inequality is graphed? Use x as a variable.

22. _____

23. Use one variable to describe the pattern of these instances.

$(2 \cdot 3)^2 = 4 \cdot 3^2$

$\left(2 \cdot \frac{1}{2}\right)^2 = 4 \cdot \left(\frac{1}{2}\right)^2$

$(2 \cdot 3.5)^2 = 4 \cdot 3.5^2$

23. _____

24. Translate into mathematics: the sum of a number n and five.

24. _____

25. You weigh 12 kg less than your brother does. If he weighs k kilograms, how much do you weigh?

25. _____

26. Recall the formula for the area of a rectangle with length ℓ and width w: $A = \ell w$. This page is $8\frac{1}{2}''$ by $11''$. What is its area?

26. _____

In 27-31, write each as a decimal.

27. 5.6 million

27. _____

28. 2.5^3

28. _____

29. 250%

29. _____

30. $-3\frac{1}{6}$

30. _____

31. $7.2 \cdot 10^{-6}$

31. _____

In 32-34, draw a figure for the description.

32. acute $\angle MAN$

32.

33. perpendicular lines $\overleftrightarrow{GO}$ and $\overleftrightarrow{TO}$

33.

34. segment IM with length 3.5 cm

34.

Now check all your work carefully.

QUIZ

1. What is a *problem?*

_____

_____

2. What is one recommendation you would make to a friend who is working on a problem?

_____

_____

3. How many triangles are formed by drawing diagonals in a rectangle?

3. _____

4. What day of the week will be 60 days from Tuesday?

4. _____

5. Exactly one of these statements is true about a given number:

   a. The number is prime.

   b. The number is not a perfect square.

   c. The number is odd.

What is the number: 167, 168, or 169?

5. _____

6. Give all the positive integer factors of 24.

6. _____

7. A piece of notebook paper measures $8\frac{1}{2}$ inches by 11 inches. If the margin is 1 inch on the top and sides and $1\frac{1}{2}$ inches on the bottom, what is the area of the working surface of the paper?

7. _____

QUIZ

In 1-3, show all work done in solving the problem.

1. The product of two positive integers is 192 and their quotient is 3. What is the larger integer?

1. _____

2. A circular pizza is cut into equal, pie-shaped pieces. Make a table showing the degree measure of the central angle for 2, 3, 4, 5 and *n* pieces.

2. _____

3. The cost for a cellular phone is $25 a month plus 35 cents per minute. What is the monthly bill for $1\frac{1}{2}$ hours of calls? For *n* hours of calls?

3. _____

In 4-6, this spreadsheet is used to give the values of
$10 + 3x - 4x^2$ **for integer values of** *x* **between -3 and 3.**

4. Fill in the rest of the spreadsheet.

4.

	A	B
1	-3	
2	-2	
3		
4		
5		
6		
7		

5. What formula could be used to fill in cell B1?

5. _____

6. After using the formula in line 7, what command would make filling in the rest of column B easy?

6. _____

CHAPTER 6 TEST, Form A

1. Name two places to find the meaning of the word *skew*.

   1. _____

2. List all prime numbers p such that $50 < p < 60$.

   2. _____

3. A hexagon has how many diagonals?

   3. _____

4. *Multiple choice.* Which is *not* good advice for problem solving?

   (a) Ask for help if you need it.

   (b) Don't give up.

   (c) Go as fast as you can.

   (d) Be flexible.

   4. _____

5. As you drive down Main Street, you first pass the library, then the high school, then the hospital, and finally the municipal swimming pool. If it is 1.7 km from the library to the hospital, 1.5 km from the high school to the pool, and .6 km from the high school to the hospital, how far is it from the library to the pool?

   5. _____

6. In a triangle, two line segments are drawn from one vertex to the opposite side of the triangle. Into how many regions do the segments split the triangle?

   6. _____

7. Both m and n are positive integers less than 6. If $m^n = 4m$, find m and n.

   7. _____

8. *Multiple choice.* Which is a solution to $2x^2 - 6x - 8 = 12$?

   (a) 4   (b) 5

   (c) 6   (d) 7

   8. _____

9. What two positive integers whose product is 32 have the largest sum?

   9. _____

10. *Multiple choice.* Which best describes the pattern $-(a + b) = -a - b$?

    (a) only sometimes true   (b) always true

    (c) always false

    10. _____

11. To multiply n by 25, first divide n by four, then move the decimal point ___?___ places to the ___?___.

    11. _____

    _____

In 12-14, use the following information. It costs $19.95 a day plus 11 cents a mile to rent a van.

12. Fill in the spreadsheet to show the cost of renting the van for one day and driving for 10, 20, 30, . . . , *n* miles.

12.

	A	B
1	miles	
2	10	
3		
4		
5		

13. What formula could be entered in cell A3?

13. _____

14. What formula should be in cell B5?

14. _____

In 15-17, show your work.

15. A cube with 4-centimeter edges is painted green and then cut into cubes with 1-centimeter edges. How many of the small cubes have no green sides?

15. _____

16. Use the statement $x^2 + y^2 = (x + y)^2$.

    a. Find a pair of values for *x* and *y* that make the statement true.

16. a. _____

    b. Find a pair of values for *x* and *y* that make the statement false.

       b. _____

17. Find a formula for the sum of the first *n* odd numbers. (Hint: the first odd number is 1, so when $n = 1$, the sum is 1. The sum of the first two odd numbers is $1 + 3$, so when $n = 2$, the sum is 4.)

17. _____

Now check all your work carefully.

CHAPTER 6 TEST, Form B

1. Name two places to find the meaning of the word *algorithm*.

1. _____

2. List all prime numbers p such that $60 < p < 70$.

2. _____

3. A heptagon has how many diagonals?

3. _____

4. *Multiple choice.* Which is *not* good advice for problem solving?

4. _____

   (a) Take your time. (b) Don't give up.

   (c) Read carefully. (d) Don't ask for help.

5. As you drive down Main Street, first you pass the library, then the high school, then the hospital, and finally the municipal swimming pool. If it is 1.3 km from the library to the hospital, 2.0 km from the high school to the pool, and .8 km from the high school to the hospital, how far is it from the library to the pool?

5. _____

6. In a pentagon, line segments are drawn from one vertex to each other vertex. Into how many regions is the pentagon split?

6. _____

7. m and n are two different positive integers less than 6. If $m^n = n^m$, find m and n.

7. _____

8. *Multiple choice.* Which is a solution to $x^2 - 6x - 8 = -13$?

8. _____

   (a) 4 (b) 5

   (c) 6 (d) 7

9. What two positive integers whose product is 32 have the smallest sum?

9. _____

10. *Multiple choice.* Which best describes the pattern $\frac{1}{a} + \frac{1}{a} = \frac{1}{2a}$?

10. _____

    (a) only sometimes true (b) always true

    (c) always false

11. To divide n by 250, first multiply n by four, then move the decimal point ___?___ place(s) to the ___?___.

11. _____

    _____

In 12-14, use the following information. It costs $29.95 a day plus 9 cents a mile to rent a van.

12. Fill in the spreadsheet to show the cost of renting the van for one day and driving for 10, 20, 30, . . . , *n* miles.

12.

	A	B
1	miles	
2	10	
3		
4		
5		

13. What formula could be entered in cell A3?

13. _____

14. What formula should be in cell B5?

14. _____

In 15-17, show your work.

15. A cube with 5-centimeter edges is painted green and then cut into cubes with 1-centimeter edges. How many of the small cubes have no green sides?

15. _____

16. Use the statement $(2 + x)^2 = 4 + y^2$.

   a. Find a pair of values for *x* and *y* that make the statement true.

16. a. _____

   b. Find a pair of values for *x* and *y* that make the statement false.

   b. _____

17. Find a formula for the sum of the first *n* even numbers. (Hint: the first even number is 2, so when $n = 1$, the sum is 2. The sum of the first two even numbers is $2 + 4$, so when $n = 2$, the sum is 6.)

17. _____

Now check all your work carefully.

CHAPTER 6 TEST, Form C

1. When $a = 2$, $a^2 = 4$ and $2a = 4$. So, your friend says this is proof that a^2 has the same meaning as $2a$. Is your friend correct? Explain why or why not.

2. Make up a real-life problem that you could solve using this diagram. Then show how to use the diagram to solve your problem.

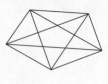

3. Refer to the chart at the right. What do you think is meant by a *semiprime number?* Write a definition of the term. Use your definition to explain why 9 is *not* semiprime. Then name four semiprime numbers that are not listed.

   The following are the first ten semiprime numbers.

6	(because 6 = 2 × 3)
10	(because 10 = 2 × 5)
14	(because 14 = 2 × 7)
15	(because 15 = 3 × 5)
21	(because 21 = 3 × 7)
22	(because 22 = 2 × 11)
26	(because 26 = 2 × 13)
33	(because 33 = 3 × 11)
34	(because 34 = 2 × 17)
35	(because 35 = 5 × 7)
38	(because 38 = 2 × 19)

4. Refer to the advertisements at the right. Is it true that you pay more to park at Acme? Or is it true that Acme has the best rates in town? Explain how you could use a handwritten table or a spreadsheet to answer these questions. Which garage would you say has the best rates?

Midtown Garage	**Acme Garage**
$4.95 first hour $.60 each additional hour	$5.45 first hour $.45 each additional hour
Why pay more at Acme?	*We have the best rates in town.*

CHAPTER 6 TEST, Form D

The table at the right displays some data about the fifty states and the District of Columbia. The data are taken from the *U.S. Bureau of the Census, Statistical Abstract of the United States: 1993*.

a. According to the first column of the table, in what region of the country do you live? In what division of that region?

b. The *Change* column of the table has been partially completed. How were the numbers in this column calculated?

c. Design a spreadsheet to display the *Resident Population* data for your region of the country. In your spreadsheet, complete the *Change* column by using a formula.

d. Add the *Land Area* data to your spreadsheet. Then add two columns to calculate and display these data:

Population Density per Square Mile, 1970

Population Density per Square Mile, 1990

e. Name several other important facts about your region that you can calculate using the given data. Adjust your spreadsheet to calculate and display these other facts.

Region, Division, and State			Resident Population			Land Area (mi²)
			1970	1990	Change	
Northeast	N.E.	ME	994,000	1,228,000	+ 234,000	30,865
		NH	738,000	1,109,000	?	8,969
		VT	445,000	563,000	?	9,249
		MA	5,689,000	6,016,000	?	7,838
		RI	950,000	1,003,000	?	1,045
		CT	3,032,000	3,287,000	?	4,845
	M.A.	NY	18,241,000	17,990,000	− 251,000	47,224
		NJ	7,171,000	7,730,000	?	7,419
		PA	11,801,000	11,882,000	?	44,820
Midwest	E.N.C.	OH	10,657,000	10,847,000	+ 190,000	40,953
		IN	5,195,000	5,544,000	?	35,870
		IL	11,110,000	11,431,000	?	55,593
		MI	8,882,000	9,295,000	?	56,809
		WI	4,418,000	4,892,000	?	54,314
	W.N.C.	MN	3,806,000	4,375,000	+ 569,000	79,617
		IA	2,825,000	2,777,000	?	55,875
		MO	4,678,000	5,117,000	?	68,898
		ND	618,000	639,000	?	68,994
		SD	666,000	696,000	?	75,896
		NE	1,485,000	1,578,000	?	76,878
		KS	2,249,000	2,478,000	?	81,823
South	S.A.	DE	548,000	666,000	+ 118,000	1,955
		MD	3,924,000	4,781,000	?	9,775
		DC	757,000	607,000	?	61
		VA	4,651,000	6,187,000	?	39,598
		WV	1,744,000	1,793,000	?	24,087
		NC	5,084,000	6,629,000	?	48,718
		SC	2,591,000	3,487,000	?	30,111
		GA	4,588,000	6,478,000	?	57,919
		FL	6,791,000	12,938,000	?	53,997
	E.S.C.	KY	3,221,000	3,685,000	+ 464,000	39,732
		TN	3,926,000	4,877,000	?	41,219
		AL	3,444,000	4,041,000	?	50,750
		MS	2,217,000	2,573,000	?	46,914
	W.S.C.	AR	1,923,000	2,351,000	+ 428,000	52,075
		LA	3,645,000	4,220,000	?	43,566
		OK	2,559,000	3,146,000	?	68,679
		TX	11,199,000	16,987,000	?	261,914
West	Mt.	MT	694,000	799,000	+ 105,000	145,556
		ID	713,000	1,007,000	?	82,751
		WY	332,000	454,000	?	97,105
		CO	2,210,000	3,294,000	?	103,729
		NM	1,017,000	1,515,000	?	121,364
		AZ	1,775,000	3,665,000	?	113,642
		UT	1,059,000	1,723,000	?	82,168
		NV	489,000	1,202,000	?	109,806
	Pac.	WA	3,413,000	4,867,000	+ 1,454,000	66,581
		OR	2,092,000	2,842,000	?	96,002
		CA	19,971,000	29,760,000	?	155,973
		AK	303,000	550,000	?	570,374
		HI	770,000	1,108,000	?	6,423

CHAPTER 6 TEST, Cumulative Form

1. If c is a composite number, list all solutions to $50 < c < 60$.

    1. _____

2. To divide by .0001, move the decimal point __?__ place(s) to the __?__ .

    2. _____

    _____

3. *Multiple choice.* Which number is a solution to $|x| > x?$

    (a) 5   (b) $\frac{1}{2}$

    (c) 0   (d) -3

    3. _____

4. Name two places you could look to find the meaning of *convex polygon*.

    4. _____

    _____

In 5-7, show your work even if you cannot finish the problem.

5. Consider the pattern $5(x + y) = 5x + y$. Is this always true? Support your answer with evidence.

    5. _____

    _____

6. What is the maximum number of intersection points five lines can have?

    6. _____

7. A rectangular garden 10 feet by 16 feet is surrounded by a walkway 2 feet wide. How long is a fence which follows the outside edge of the walkway?

    7. _____

▶ **CHAPTER 6 TEST, Cumulative Form** *page 2*

8. The rate for a call to Malaysia from the United States is $2.98 for the first minute and $1.12 for each additional minute between 2 A.M. and 11 A.M. It costs $2.38 for the first minute and $.85 for each additional minute between 11 A.M. and 5 P.M. Additional-minute costs change if a call goes from one time period to another. Design a spreadsheet to show the cost after each 5-minute segment for a call that began at 10:45 A.M. and finished at 11:30 A.M.

8.

	A	B	C
1			
2			
3			
4			
5			
6			
7			
8			
9			

9. $\frac{2}{3} + -\frac{1}{9} = $ _____?_____

9. _____

10. Simplify: $x + -y + -x$

10. _____

11. Evaluate $(2p - 3)^3$ when $p = 2.5$.

11. _____

12. *Multiple choice.* Which number is *not* equal to the others?

   (a) $\frac{3}{5}$ (b) 6×10^{-1}

   (c) 60%   (d) $.\overline{6}$

12. _____

13. Write as a decimal: 10^{-4}

13. _____

14. Solve: $-3 + x = 2\frac{1}{2}$

14. _____

15. On Thursday, July 8, 1993, the Dow Jones Industrial average jumped 38.75 points to a value of 3514.42. What was the value on July 7?

15. _____

16. Write $\frac{3.5}{100}$ as

    a. a decimal.

16. **a.** _____

    b. a percent.

       b. _____

17. Draw a triangle with three acute angles.

17.

18. All Star Middle School claims that 85% of its students participate in at least one activity in addition to classes. If the school has 323 students, how many participate in at least one activity in addition to classes?

18. _____

19. Name a problem-solving strategy.

19. _____

_____

20. Explain when to try the strategy you named in Question 19 and how to use it.

_____

_____

_____

Now check all your work carefully.

COMPREHENSIVE TEST, Chapters 1-6

You will need a protractor and a ruler marked in inches and centimeters.

In 1-25, *multiple choice*. Give the letter of the correct answer.

1. Rounded to the nearest ten-thousandth, .1234567 is ___?___.
   (a) .10000   (b) .1234
   (c) .1235   (d) .12346

   1. _____

2. Which sign belongs in the blank? -5 ___?___ -2.4
   (a) >   (b) <
   (c) =   (d) ≈

   2. _____

3. $\frac{11}{12}$ = ___?___
   (a) .916   (b) .9166667
   (c) .91$\overline{6}$ (d) $.9\overline{16}$

   3. _____

4. $\frac{6.3}{9}$ = ___?___
   (a) $\frac{63}{9}$ (b) 7
   (c) $\frac{7}{10}$ (d) .07

   4. _____

5. 58.6 million = ___?___
   (a) 58,000,006   (b) 58,000,000.6
   (c) 58.6,000,000   (d) 58,600,000

   5. _____

6. .000059 = ___?___
   (a) 5.9×10^{-5} (b) 5.9×10^{-6}
   (c) 5.9×10^{-7} (d) 5.9×10^{-8}

   6. _____

7. $\frac{9}{16}$ = ___?___
   (a) 56.25   (b) .5625%
   (c) 5.625   (d) $56\frac{1}{4}$%

   7. _____

8. 250% of 30 = ___?___
   (a) 7.5   (b) 75
   (c) .75   (d) 750

   8. _____

9. $\frac{1}{4}$ gallon = ___?___
   (a) 1 quart   (b) 1 pint
   (c) 1 cup   (d) 1 ounce

   9. _____

Name _____

10. 1 kilogram = ___?___   **10.** _____

   (a) 1000 milligrams   (b) 100 milligrams

   (c) 10,000,000 milligrams (d) 1,000,000 milligrams

11. The angle formed by the corner of this page is ___?___.   **11.** _____

   (a) an acute angle   (b) a right angle

   (c) a straight angle   (d) an obtuse angle

12. A square foot contains   **12.** _____

   (a) 12 in.   (b) 12 in.²

   (c) 144 in.   (d) 144 in.²

13. $15 - 3 \cdot 2 + 1 =$ ___?___   **13.** _____

   (a) 10   (b) 36

   (c) 25   (d) 6

14. Three less than the square of a number can be written as ___?___.   **14.** _____

   (a) $3 - n^2$ (b) $3 < n^2$

   (c) $n^2 - 3$ (d) $2n - 3$

15. If $m = 5$ and $n = -6$, then $3m + n =$ ___?___.   **15.** _____

   (a) 29   (b) 9

   (c) 2   (d) 21

16. $6(12 + -8)^2 =$ ___?___   **16.** _____

   (a) 96   (b) 576

   (c) 616   (d) 136

17. If $a^{-2} = \dfrac{1}{a^2}$, then $5^{-2} =$ ___?___.   **17.** _____

   (a) -25   (b) 25

   (c) $-\dfrac{1}{25}$ (d) $\dfrac{1}{25}$

18. The inequality represented by this graph is   **18.** _____

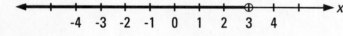

   (a) $x < 3$ (b) $x \le 3$

   (c) $x > 3$ (d) $x \ge 3$

19. $4 + \dfrac{5}{6} =$ ___?___   **19.** _____

   (a) $\dfrac{45}{6}$ (b) $\dfrac{20}{6}$

   (c) $\dfrac{29}{6}$ (d) $\dfrac{24}{6}$

20. The additive identity is ___?___.   20. _____

    (a) 1   (b) n

    (c) 0   (d) $\frac{1}{n}$

21. $|-2\frac{1}{2}| + |3\frac{2}{3}| = $ ___?___   21. _____

    (a) $5\frac{1}{6}$ (b) $6\frac{1}{6}$

    (c) $1\frac{1}{6}$ (d) $-1\frac{1}{6}$

22. An eight-sided polygon is called ___?___.   22. _____

    (a) a pentagon   (b) a hexagon

    (c) an octagon   (d) a rhombus

23. If gas costs $1.37 per gallon, then 10.4 gallons will cost ___?___.   23. _____

    (a) $14.24   (b) $14.25

    (c) $1.42   (d) $2.38

24. The franc is a unit of French money. If $1 = 5.73 francs, how many francs would you get for $75?   24. _____

    (a) 42.975   (b) 429.75

    (c) 13.09   (d) 131

25. When you toss a six-sided die, what is the probability that you will get an odd number?   25. _____

    (a) $\frac{1}{6}$ (b) $\frac{1}{3}$

    (c) $\frac{1}{2}$ (d) $\frac{5}{6}$

26. A scholarship awards $1000 to a qualifying student. To qualify, the student's family income must be less than 175% of the official poverty level. The 1990 poverty level for a family of four was $13,359. In order for a student to qualify that year for the scholarship, what was the highest possible income that a student's family could earn?   26. _____

27. How many miles is a 50,000-m bike race?   27. _____

28. In △*GNP*, use a ruler and a protractor to find

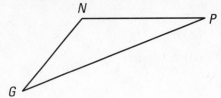

    a. *GN* to the nearest millimeter.

    b. m ∠*N*.

28. a. _____

     b. _____

29. Find the area of this rectangle.

6 in. [   ]

       4 feet

29. _____

30. Translate into mathematics using *n* for the number.

    a. 10 less than a number

    b. 10 less a number

    c. 10 is less than a number.

30. a. _____

     b. _____

     c. _____

31. Solve $2 + k + \text{-}6 = \text{-}2$. Show your work.

31. _____

32. Jack is taller than Jill. Jill is shorter than Joan. Joan is taller than Jordan. Jordan is taller than Jack. Who is the second tallest?

32. _____

33. Describe two advantages of a computer spreadsheet.

_____

_____

_____

Now check all your work carefully.

QUIZ

In 1-4, simplify.

1. -6 − 24

2. 7.25 − -7.25

3. $3\frac{1}{2} - 6\frac{1}{4}$

4. $\frac{2}{3} - .6$

1. _____

2. _____

3. _____

4. _____

In 5-8, solve. Show your work.

5. $b - 63 = 45$ 6. -17.2 = N − -6.25

7. $3 + K - 14 = -1$ 8. $\frac{17}{12} - y = -\frac{21}{24}$

5. _____

6. _____

7. _____

8. _____

In 9-10,
a. write an equation, and
b. answer the question.

9. One type of toad has been found on mountains at heights of around 26,200 feet and in coal mines around 1,100 feet below the ground. What is the difference in these elevations?

9. a. _____

   b. _____

10. In the Great Train Robbery on August 8, 1963, in Glasgow, $7.41 million worth of banknotes was stolen. About $960,000 was recovered. How much was never found?

10. a. _____

    b. _____

11. What is the area of the shaded region between the two squares?

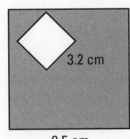

3.2 cm

9.5 cm

11. _____

12. Is subtraction commutative? Justify your answer.

_____

_____

QUIZ

In 1 and 2, show your work.

1. At Seaview High School, 246 seniors take math, 122 take computer science, 83 take both courses, and 32 take neither course. How many seniors attend Seaview High?

1. _____

2. If you toss a pair of dice, find the probability that you will get a sum of 8 or a double.

2. _____

In 3-6, find the measure of each angle without using a protractor.

3. m ∠ 1   5. m ∠ 5

4. m ∠ 3   6. m ∠ 6

3. _____

4. _____

5. _____

6. _____

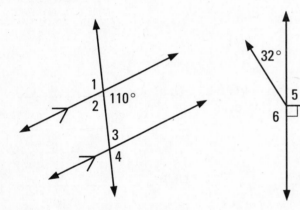

In 7-10, use the figure below.

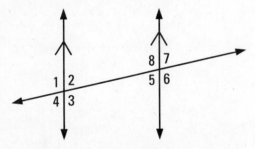

7. Name one pair of vertical angles.

7. _____

8. Name one linear pair.

8. _____

9. Name one pair of corresponding angles.

9. _____

10. Name one pair of alternate exterior angles.

10. _____

CHAPTER 7 TEST, Form A

In 1-5, simplify.

1. $3 - 7$

2. $-2.5 - 8$

3. $\frac{1}{2} - -\frac{3}{4}$

4. $-8 - -15.8 - 6 - -3.1$.

5. $2\frac{1}{2} - 5\frac{5}{6}$

1. _____

2. _____

3. _____

4. _____

5. _____

In 6-8, solve each equation. Show your work.

6. $P - 8 = -4$

6. _____

7. $-2 - Q = 29$

7. _____

8. $2(3.5) = 5 - R - 10$

8. _____

In 9 and 10, a question is asked.
a. Write an equation whose solution answers the question.
b. Solve your equation.
c. Give your answer in a sentence.

9. Ribbon Falls in California, the highest waterfall in the U.S., is 1600 feet lower than Angel Falls in Venezuela, the highest in the world. If Ribbon Falls is 1612 feet high, how high is Angel Falls?

9. a. _____

   b. _____

   c. _____

   _____

   _____

10. The temperature at 6 P.M. was -40° F. At 2 A.M., it was -13° F. How much did the temperature change?

10. a. _____

    b. _____

    c. _____

    _____

    _____

11. Write three sentences equivalent to $a - x = b$.

11. _____

    _____

    _____

12. Refer to the figure at the right. Without using a protractor, find

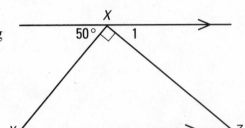

a. m ∠ 1.

12. a. _____

b. m ∠ Y.

    b. _____

c. m ∠ Z.

    c. _____

13. Two angles in a triangle measure 29° and 79°. What is the measure of the third angle?

13. _____

14. Use the figure at the right to fill in each blank.

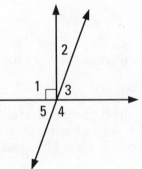

a. m ∠ 1 + m ∠ 2 = m ∠ ___?___

14. a. _____

b. If m ∠ 3 = 70°, m ∠ 2 = ___?___.

    b. _____

c. If m ∠ 3 = 70°, m ∠ 4 = ___?___.

    c. _____

15. The figure at the right is composed of two squares. What is the area of the shaded region?

15. _____

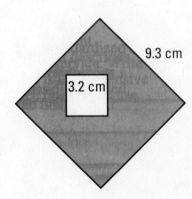

9.3 cm

3.2 cm

16. Evaluate $a - b - (c - d)$ when $a = -1$, $b = 3$, $c = -2$, and $d = 2$.

16. _____

17. Suppose in a school of 800 students, 13% earned an A in science, 17% earned an A in math, and 4% earned an A in both science and math. Draw a Venn diagram to illustrate this situation.

17.

18. If you choose a card from a standard 52-card deck, what is the probability that you will choose a face card or a red card?

18. _____

19. Draw a pair of parallel lines and a transversal. Pick an angle and mark all angles which are equal to it.

19.

In 20-22, *true or false.*

20. All rectangles are parallelograms.

20. _____

21. All parallelograms are rectangles.

21. _____

22. All squares are rhombuses.

22. _____

23. If *ABCD* is a parallelogram, then m $\angle A$ = m $\angle$ ___?___.

23. _____

24. Explain why a triangle cannot have more than one obtuse angle.

_____

_____

25. **a.** Picture the subtraction $-8 - 3$ on this number line.

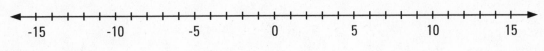

b. Give the result.

25. b. _____

Now check all your work carefully.

CHAPTER 7 TEST, Form B

In 1-5, simplify.

1. $6 - 12$

2. $-2 - 4.3$

3. $\frac{1}{4} - -\frac{5}{8}$

4. $-8 - -15.8 - 6 - -3.1$

5. $4\frac{6}{7} - 5\frac{11}{14}$

1. _____

2. _____

3. _____

4. _____

5. _____

In 6-8, solve each equation. Show your work.

6. $P - 6 = -7$

6. _____

7. $-5 - Q = 16$

7. _____

8. $4(2.5) = 15 - R - 25$

8. _____

In 9 and 10, a question is asked.
a. Write an equation for each situation.
b. Solve your equation.
c. Give your answer in a sentence.

9. The Bank of China building in Hong Kong is 245 feet lower than the Sears Tower in Chicago. If the Sears Tower is 1454 feet high, how high is the Bank of China building?

9. a. _____

   b. _____

   c. _____

10. The temperature at 6 P.M. was -4° C. At 2 A.M., it was -13° C. How much did the temperature change?

10. a. _____

b. _____

c. _____

11. Write three sentences equivalent to $x + b = a$.

11. _____

_____

_____

12. Refer to the figure at the right. Without using a protractor, find

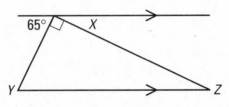

a. m $\angle X$.

b. m $\angle Y$.

c. m $\angle Z$.

12. a. _____

b. _____

c. _____

13. Two angles in a triangle measure 35° and 128°. What is the measure of the third angle?

13. _____

14. Use the figure at the right to fill in each blank.

a. m $\angle 1$ + m $\angle 2$ = m $\angle$ ___?___

b. If m $\angle 3 = 40°$, m $\angle 2 =$ ___?___ .

c. If m $\angle 3 = 40°$, m $\angle 4 =$ ___?___ .

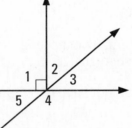

14. a. _____

b. _____

c. _____

15. The figure at the right is composed of two squares. What is the area of the shaded region?

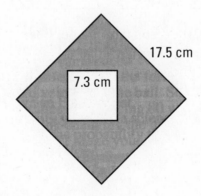

17.5 cm

7.3 cm

15. _____

16. Evaluate $a - b - (c - d)$ when $a = $ -4, $b = 6$, $c = $ -3, and $d = 4$.

16. _____

17. Suppose in a school of 600 students, 15% earned an A in science, 12% earned an A in math, and 7% earned an A in both science and math. Draw a Venn diagram to illustrate this situation.

17.

18. If you choose a card from a standard 52-card deck, what is the probability that you will choose a jack or a club?

18. _____

19. Draw a pair of parallel lines and a transversal. Mark all equal angles.

19.

In 20-22, *true or false.*

20. All squares are parallelograms.

20. _____

21. All parallelograms are squares.

21. _____

22. All rectangles are rhombuses.

22. _____

23. If *ABCD* is a parallelogram, then the length of segment *BC* equals the length of segment ___?___.

23. _____

24. Explain why a triangle cannot have two right angles.

_____

_____

25. a. Picture the subtraction -10 − 5 on this number line.

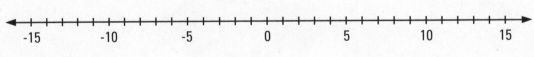

b. Give the result.

25. b. _____

Now check all your work carefully.

CHAPTER 7 TEST, Form C

1. Describe three real-world situations that you can represent by the subtraction -4 − 5. Find the difference.

2. Write two different equations that are equivalent to -2 − x = 9. Explain how you know the equations are equivalent.

3. Every student in Paulo's class has a cat or dog as a pet. Paulo says 25 students have a dog and 14 have a cat. Rita says there must be 39 students in the class. Is she correct? Use a Venn diagram to explain your answer. What is the *least* number of students in the class?

4. Quadrilateral *ABCD* is a parallelogram, with m∠*A* = 90° and *AB* = *CD*. What special type of parallelogram is *ABCD*? Be as specific as you can, and explain how you know.

5. Write ten facts about the relationships among the lines and angles that are labeled in the figure at the right.

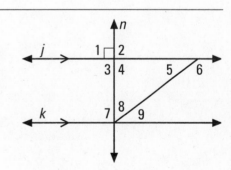

CHAPTER 7 TEST, Form D

The table at the right lists prices for one share of stock in several companies. The prices are given as fractions that represent dollars and cents. An entry like $19\frac{5}{8}$ means 19.625 *dollars,* which rounded to the nearest cent is $19.63.

a. Complete the *Change* column of the table.

b. Suppose you had $5,000 to invest in a certain stock. Divide $5,000 by the price of the stock one year ago to determine how many shares you could have purchased. You may not purchase a fraction of a share, and you may not spend more than $5,000.

c. Estimate the amount you would have gained or lost on your investment in one year.

d. Create a chart that illustrates and compares the results if $5,000 had been invested in each of these stocks exactly one year ago.

e. If you had $5,000 to invest today, in which of these stocks do you think you would invest? Explain your decision.

Stock	Close Today	Close One Year Ago	Change
BinCo	$32\frac{3}{4}$	$29\frac{1}{8}$	$+3\frac{5}{8}$
CDR	28	$25\frac{1}{4}$	$+2\frac{3}{4}$
DysH	$35\frac{7}{8}$	43	$-7\frac{1}{8}$
EngR	$18\frac{1}{2}$	$19\frac{1}{4}$	$-\frac{3}{4}$
GenCm	$48\frac{1}{8}$	$38\frac{3}{4}$	
KJCo	11	$13\frac{1}{2}$	
MasWy	$43\frac{1}{4}$	$44\frac{3}{4}$	
NSys	$22\frac{3}{4}$	18	
PCGen	$29\frac{1}{8}$	$30\frac{7}{8}$	
TynD	45	$42\frac{5}{8}$	
VNG	$16\frac{1}{4}$	$15\frac{5}{8}$	
YszCo	37	$28\frac{3}{4}$	

CHAPTER 7 TEST, Cumulative Form

In 1 and 2, a subtraction is given.
a. Explain *how* to do the subtraction without a calculator.
b. Give the answer.

1. $3 - 11$

1. a. _____

_____

_____

b. _____

2. $5 - -8$

2. a. _____

_____

_____

b. _____

3. Evaluate $7 - x - y$, when $x = 5$ and $y = -9$.

3. _____

In 4-6, solve. Show your work.

4. $f - 7.9 = -6$

4. _____

5. $-15 = 3 - y$

5. _____

6. Solve for y: $m - y = -b$

6. _____

7. Two angles of a triangle measure 31° and 49°. What is the measure of the third angle?

7. _____

8. A polygon has 10 sides of equal length and 10 angles of equal measure. What kind of polygon is it?

8. _____

9. *True or false.* All rectangles are squares.

9. _____

In 10-12, *p* ∥ *q*. **Find each measure.**

10. m ∠ 1

11. m ∠ 4

12. m ∠ 5

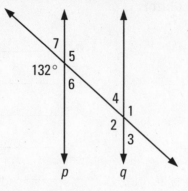

10. _____

11. _____

12. _____

13. In a rectangular garden, a square is reserved for pepper plants. Use the drawing to determine the area that remains for other plants.

13. _____

```
┌─────────────────────────────┐
│                             │
│  peppers                    │
│  ┌───┐               5 m    │
│  │   │  1.5 m               │
│  └───┘                      │
│                             │
└─────────────────────────────┘
            7 m
```

In 14 and 15, use the following information:
853 passengers rode a commuter train into the city.
642 of them had monthly passes. The remainder
t **of the passengers had to purchase tickets.**

14. Write an equation showing a relationship among these quantities.

14. _____

15. How many passengers had to purchase tickets?

15. _____

16. Mrs. Yang's math class has 28 students. Ms. Lovelace's science class has 24 students. Six students have both Mrs. Yang and Ms. Lovelace. How many students are in at least one of the two classes?

16. _____

In 17 and 18, show your work.

17. If turkey costs $1.89 per $\frac{1}{2}$ pound, what will $\frac{3}{4}$ pound cost?

17. _____

Name _____

18. Find values for x and y that make this statement false:
$|x| - |y| = |x - y|$

18. _____

In 19-24, write each as a single decimal.

19. $3 \cdot 8 - 8 \cdot 3$

19. _____

20. $\frac{81.42}{0.3}$

20. _____

21. $\frac{3}{4} - \frac{1}{6}$

21. _____

22. $8.3 \cdot 10^{-2}$

22. _____

23. 2.3 million

23. _____

24. $\boxed{2.51 \qquad 03}$

24. _____

25. What is meant by the *active cell* in a spreadsheet?

_____

_____

26. Two normal dice are tossed at the same time. Assume the
dice are fair. Let $E =$ both dice show an even number.
Let $C =$ one of the dice shows a 2.

a. What is the probability of event *E?*

26. a. _____

b. What is the probability of event *C?*

b. _____

c. Are the events *E* and *C* mutually exclusive?

c. _____

Now check all your work carefully.

QUIZ

In 1–3, graph the points on the coordinate graph. Label each point.

1. $A = (4, -3)$

2. $B = (0, 2)$

3. $C = (-1, -2)$

1.–3.

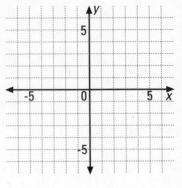

4. Refer to Question 1. In which quadrant is point A?

4. _____

In 5 and 6, use the graph.

Participation in 10 Most Popular Sports in 1990

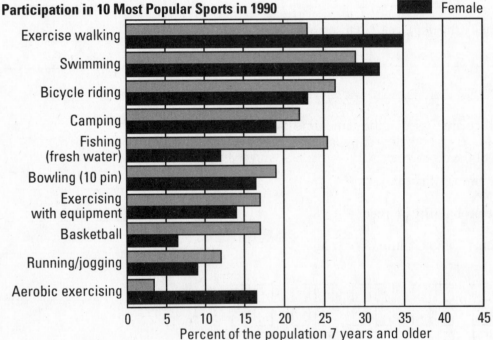

Male
Female

Percent of the population 7 years and older

5. In which of these activities do more females participate than males?

5. _____

6. What is the interval on the horizontal axis?

6. _____

7. Explain why someone might prefer a graph to a table with numbers.

_____

_____

Name _____

QUIZ

1. Graph the line with equation $x + y = 3$. List values for x and y in the table.

x	y

1.

2. **a.** Graph the quadrilateral with vertices $(2, 5)$, $(4, 1)$, $(3, -1)$ and $(-3, -2)$.

   b. Change each first coordinate to its opposite and graph the new quadrilateral.

   c. Label the image and the pre-image.

2. a–c.

   d. The pre-image can be reflected over what line to obtain the image?

d. _____

3. Is triangle ABC congruent to triangle PQR? Why or why not?

3. _____

_____

_____

_____

_____

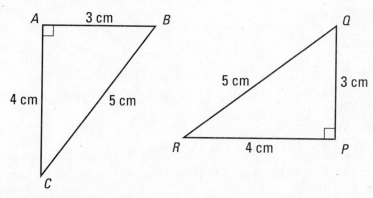

4. What happens to a figure if 2 is added to the second coordinate of each point?

_____

_____

CHAPTER 8 TEST, Form A

In 1–3, use this bar graph. It shows trading activity in a stock exchange over a 2-week period.

1. Give two reasons for using this graph.

1. _____

_____

_____

_____

_____

_____

_____

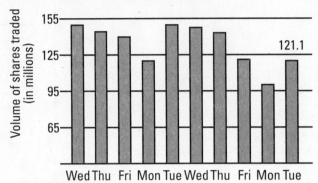

2. What was the volume of shares traded on the last day?

2. _____

3. *Multiple choice.* On which day was the lowest volume of shares traded?

3. _____

(a) the first Monday   (b) the second Monday

(c) the first Wednesday   (d) the second Thursday

In 4–6, use this information: Students in a math class received the following scores on the last test.

94, 93, 86, 87, 80, 79, 61, 54, 67, 78, 93, 77, 93, 88, 71, 84, 70, 63, 72, 75, 78

4. Show the information in a stem-and-leaf display.

4.

5. a. What is the range of these test scores?

5. a. _____

b. What is the median of these test scores?

b. _____

c. What is the mode of these test scores?

c. _____

6. Assume that a grading scale is as follows:

6.

A, 85–100; **B,** 72–84; **C,** 60–71; **D,** 50–59; **F,** below 50

Display the grades using a bar graph which shows the number of students earning each grade.

Name _____

7. *True or false.* A figure and its reflection image are not congruent.

7. _____

In 8–10, use the graph shown.

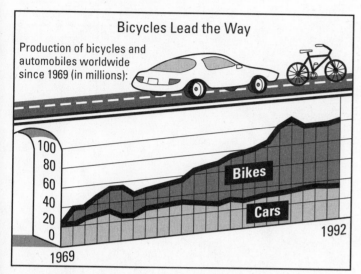

8. What does 80 on the vertical scale represent?

8. _____

9. How many bicycles were produced in 1980?

9. _____

10. In which year was the difference between bicycle and car production greatest? What was the difference?

10. _____

_____

11. Graph these points:

$A = (0, 4), B = (5, -3), C = (-2, -4),$
$D = (-1, 0), E = (4, -4)$

11.

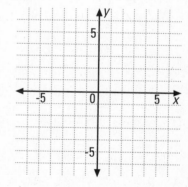

12. Graph the line with equation $x - y = -1$.
List values for x and y in the table.

x	y

12.

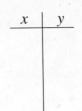

13. Display the following information on the grid at the right.

If one math problem takes 2 minutes to complete, Nancy will complete 30 problems.

If one math problem takes 3 minutes to complete, Nancy will complete 20 problems.

If one math problem takes 5 minutes to complete, Nancy will complete 12 problems.

If one math problem takes 10 minutes to complete, Nancy will complete 6 problems.

13.

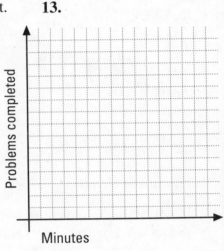

14. Draw in all lines of symmetry for each letter at the right.

14. a.

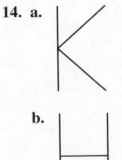

b.

15. Sketch a tessellation using this figure. Show enough to make the tessellation clear.

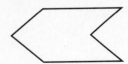

15.

16. Draw the reflection image of the triangle over line *m*.

16.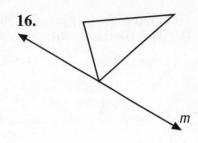

In 17-19, the image of (*x, y*) is (*x* - 2, *y* - 1).

17. Name the image of each point under this transformation.

    a. (1, 2)

    b. (2, 0)

    c. (1, -2)

17. a. _____

    b. _____

    c. _____

18. Graph the preimage points (1, 2), (2, 0), and (1, -2) and connect them in order. Then graph the image points and connect them in the same order.

18.

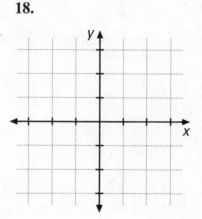

19. What type of transformation is illustrated in Question 18?

19. _____

20. *R'* is the reflection image of point *R* over line *ℓ*. Answer with numbers.

    a. m ∠ *R'ST* = ___?___

    b. If *RS* = 9, then *R'S* = ___?___.

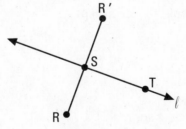

20. a. _____

    b. _____

Now check all your work carefully.

CHAPTER 8 TEST, Form B

In 1-3, use the bar graph below. It shows the energy in thousands of BTUs (British thermal units) needed to make several types of 12-oz containers.

1. Give two reasons for using this graph.

1. _____

_____

_____

_____

_____

_____

_____

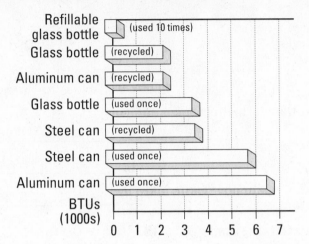

2. How much energy is needed to make a recycled aluminum can?

2. _____

3. *Multiple choice.* The most energy is saved in recycling which type of container?

3. _____

    (a) aluminum can   (b) glass bottle (recycled)

    (c) steel can   (d) glass bottle (used 10 times)

In 4-6, use this information: Students in a science class received the following scores on the last test.

95, 96, 81, 88, 88, 92, 65, 49, 72, 85, 84, 92, 97, 83, 86, 84, 75, 79, 81, 96, 63, 100

4. Show the information in a stem-and-leaf display.

4.

5. a. What is the range of these test scores?

5. a. _____

   b. What is the median of these test scores?

b. _____

   c. What is the mode of these test scores?

c. _____

6. Assume that a grading scale is as follows:

   A, 85–100; **B,** 72–84; **C,** 60–71; **D,** 50–59; **F,** below 50

   Display the grades using a bar graph which shows the number of students earning each grade.

6.

7. *True or false.* A figure and its reflection image are not congruent.

7. _____

In 8-10, use the graph shown.

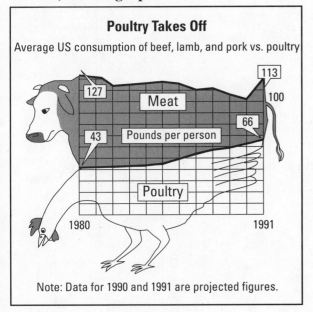

Poultry Takes Off

Average US consumption of beef, lamb, and pork vs. poultry

127
113
100
Meat
66
43
Pounds per person
Poultry
1980
1991

Note: Data for 1990 and 1991 are projected figures.

8. What does 100 on the vertical scale represent?

8. _____

9. On the average, how many pounds of poultry were consumed per person in the U.S. in 1985?

9. _____

10. In 1989 how much more meat than poultry was consumed by the average person?

10. _____

11. Graph these points:

$A = (3, 2), B = (0, -6), C = (-6, -5),$
$D = (-5, 3), E = (0, 0)$

11.

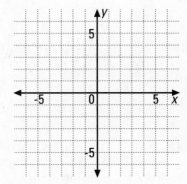

12. Graph the line with equation $x + y = 4$.
List values for x and y in the table.

12.

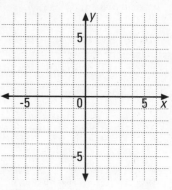

13. Display the following information on the grid at the right.

If one math problem takes 2 minutes to complete, Gary will complete 12 problems.

If one math problem takes 3 minutes to complete, Gary will complete 8 problems.

If one math problem takes 6 minutes to complete, Gary will complete 4 problems.

If one math problem takes 12 minutes to complete, Gary will complete 2 problems.

13.

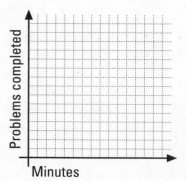

14. Draw in all lines of symmetry for each letter.

14. a.

b.

15. Sketch a tessellation using this figure. Show enough to make the tessellation clear.

15.

16. Draw the reflection image of each short segment over line *m*.

16.

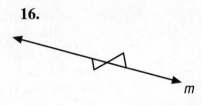

In 17-19, the image of (x, y) **is** $(x + 3, y + 1)$.

17. Name the image of each point under this transformation.

    a. $(0, 0)$

    b. $(-1, 2)$

    c. $(-3, -3)$

17. a. _____

    b. _____

    c. _____

18. Graph the preimage points $(0, 0)$, $(-1, 2)$, and $(-3, -3)$ and connect them in order. Then graph the image points and connect them in the same order.

18.

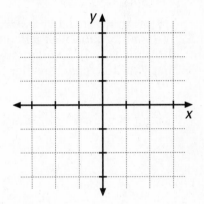

19. What type of transformation is illustrated in Question 18?

19. _____

20. R' is the reflection image of point R over line ℓ. Answer with numbers.

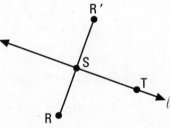

    a. m $\angle RST$ = ___?___

    b. If $RS = 12$, then
       $R'S$ = ___?___ .

20. a. _____

    b. _____

Now check all your work carefully.

CHAPTER 8 TEST, Form C

1. Create a set of twelve numbers that satisfy the following conditions.

    The range is 41.
    The median is 25.
    The mode is 11.

    Make a stem-and-leaf display of your data.

2. Mai Lin has collected data about the cost of a one-day video rental at ten different stores in her town. Why do you think it might help to display the costs in a graph? What type of graph do you think she should use? Explain your choice.

3. Write an equation for a line that contains the point (-1, 4). Explain how you know that your line contains that point.

4. Complete the figure below so that line *m* is a line of symmetry. Then draw *all* lines of symmetry of your completed figure.

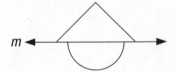

5. Suppose your friend is having difficulty understanding the difference between a *translation image* and a *reflection image* and has asked for your help. Use the figure at the right to write an explanation for your friend.

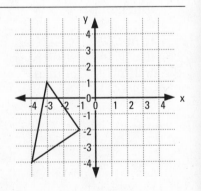

Your parents are planning to pave a rectangular patio floor with bricks. The floor is 5 feet wide and 7 feet long. The top surface of each brick is a rectangle that is 4 inches wide and 8 inches long.

Your parents have asked for your help in planning an attractive pattern for the floor. The figures on this page show seven patterns that are commonly used by bricklayers.

a. Which figures have reflection symmetry? Draw all the lines of symmetry in these figures.

b. Which figure is formed by translations of the basic L-shape shown at the right?

c. According to the definition of tessellation that you learned, which figure does *not* show a tessellation? Explain.

d. Choose one of the patterns on this page, or create your own original pattern. On graph paper, make a drawing that shows how the patio will look when it is completely covered with bricks arranged in your pattern. (You may need to use parts of bricks in some places.)

e. How many bricks are needed to cover the patio floor using the pattern you chose?

f. Bricks cost 58¢ each at your local building supply store. When you buy the bricks, you should get between 5% and 10% more than the plan shows to allow for breakage. Using this information, estimate the cost of the bricks needed for the patio floor.

Jack-on-Jack

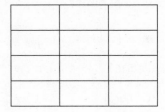

Traditional

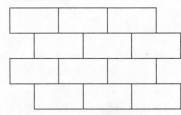

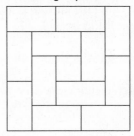

Whorling Square

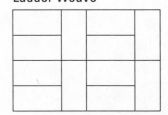

Ladder Weave

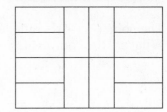

Herringbone

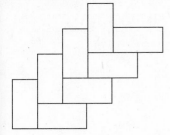

Half Basket

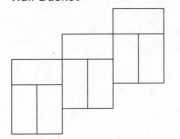

Basket Weave Variation

CHAPTER 8 TEST, Cumulative Form

In 1-3, use the bar graph below that appeared in a July 1, 1993, newspaper.

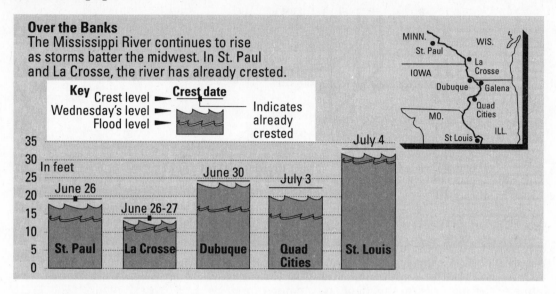

1. In which city shown was the Mississippi River farthest above flood level?

1. _____

2. What was the flood level in St. Louis, Missouri?

2. _____

3. Which cities were still waiting for the river to crest?

3. _____

4. Draw all lines of symmetry.

4.

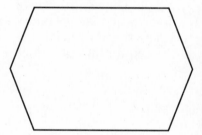

5. Name a quadrilateral that has 4 lines of symmetry.

5. _____

6. The point (-2, -4) is reflected over the y-axis. What are the coordinates of its image?

6. _____

7. **a.** In which quadrant is point *A*?

   b. Give the coordinates of point *A*.

7. **a.** _____

    b. _____

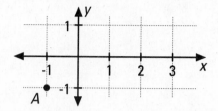

8. Draw the reflection image of triangle *PNO* over line *m*.

8.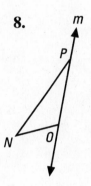

9. Draw a tessellation using the figure at the right as the fundamental region. Make the pattern clear.

9.

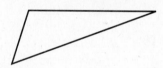

10. Graph all solutions to $y - x = -3$. List values for *x* and *y* in the table.

x	y

10.

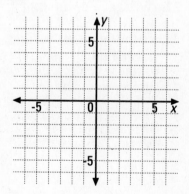

In 11 and 12, simplify.

11. $-6 - -9$

12. $x + c - y - x - c$

11. _____

12. _____

Name

In 13-15, solve for *x*. Show your work.

13. $x + \frac{5}{8} = -7$

13. _____

14. $-12 = 8 - x$

14. _____

15. $3 + x < 44$, $x > 31$, and *x* is a prime number.

15. _____

16. The side of a square tile is 7.5 in. What is its perimeter?

16. _____

17. Translate into mathematics: 6 less than the square of a number *n*

17. _____

18. How many grams is $4\,kg + 70g + 100\,mg$?

18. _____

19. What is 150% of 60?

19. _____

20. Simplify $1\frac{3}{8} + \frac{3}{5}$.

20. _____

21. Simplify $0 - -8.125$.

21. _____

22. Write as a decimal: $\frac{1}{1,000,000}$

22. _____

23. In the figure at the right, $s \parallel m$. Find the measures of the given angles. Do not use a protractor.

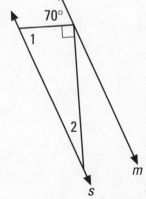

a. $m \angle 1$

23. a. _____

b. $m \angle 2$

b. _____

▶ **CHAPTER 8 TEST, Cumulative Form** *page 4*

In 24 and 25, use the two graphs showing gold and silver prices in a recent year.

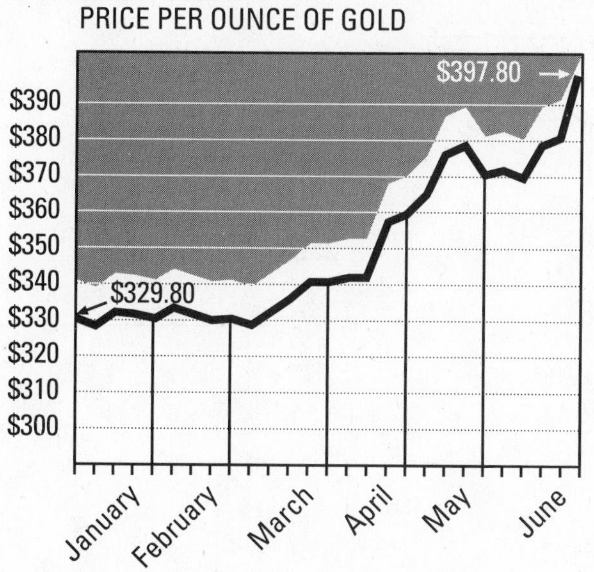

PRICE PER OUNCE OF GOLD

$397.80 →

$390
$380
$370
$360
$350
$340
$330 $329.80
$320
$310
$300

January February March April May June

PRICE PER OUNCE OF SILVER

$5.50

$5.10

$5.00

$4.50

$4.00

$3.50

$3.00

$0

January February March April May June July

24. In which month was the price of silver lowest?

24. _____

25. Examine the two graphs. Briefly describe any similarities *and* differences you notice about the trends in price changes of gold and silver.

_____

_____

_____

_____

_____

_____

_____

Now check all your work carefully.

QUIZ

1. a. Find the perimeter.   **2. a.** Find the area of the base.

 b. Find the area.   **b.** Find the volume.

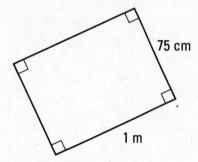

75 cm

1 m

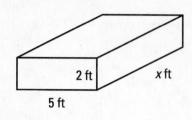

2 ft x ft

5 ft

1. a. _____

 b. _____

2. a. _____

 b. _____

**In 3-6, indicate whether the sentence illustrates
(a) the Commutative Property of Multiplication,
(b) the Associative Property of Multiplication,
(c) both properties, or
(d) neither property.**

3. $2\frac{1}{2} \cdot 6 = 2 \cdot 5 \cdot 6$

4. $\frac{3}{4} \cdot \frac{5}{7} = \frac{5}{7} \cdot \frac{3}{4}$

5. $8 \cdot 2 \cdot 5 = 8 \cdot (2 \cdot 5)$

6. $5 \cdot (3 \cdot 4) = (5 \cdot 4) \cdot 3$

3. _____

4. _____

5. _____

6. _____

In 7-10, simplify. Give answers in lowest terms.

7. $\frac{2}{5} \cdot \frac{4}{9}$ **8.** $8 \cdot \frac{5}{7}$

9. $\frac{m}{n} \cdot \frac{n}{m}$ **10.** $\frac{5}{6} \cdot 2 \cdot \frac{3}{8}$

7. _____

8. _____

9. _____

10. _____

In 11-13, give the reciprocal of each number.

11. $\frac{1}{2}$

12. $\frac{3}{8}$

13. 2.5

14. Use a rectangle to model $\frac{2}{3} \times \frac{2}{5}$. Give the answer.

11. _____

12. _____

13. _____

14. _____

QUIZ

1. The boring machine used to dig the tunnel under the English Channel could advance at a rate of 26 feet an hour. The tunnel is 31 miles long. How many hours would it have taken to bore this tunnel if the machine had operated nonstop?

1. _____

In 2 and 3, simplify.

2. $-a \cdot -1 \cdot b$

2. _____

3. $4xy + t$ when $x = -4$, $y = -3$, and $t = -10$.

3. _____

In 4 and 5, solve.

4. $0x = -8$

4. _____

5. $-16x = 0$

5. _____

6. *Multiple choice.* A size change of magnitude $\frac{7}{8}$ is a(n) ___?___ .

6. _____

   (a) rotation   (b) expansion

   (c) contraction   (d) symmetry

7., 8.

In 7 and 8, use the quadrilateral at the right.

7. Draw the image of the quadrilateral under a size change of magnitude $\frac{1}{3}$.

8. Draw the image of the quadrilateral under a size change of magnitude 2.

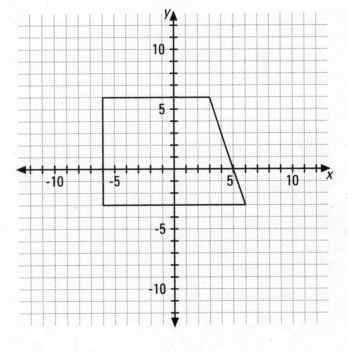

115

CHAPTER 9 TEST, Form A

1. What is the area of a rectangle 8.5 cm by 3.9 cm?

   1. _____

2. $10 \cdot (20 \cdot 30) = (10 \cdot 20) \cdot 30$ is an instance of what property?

   2. _____

3. What is the reciprocal of 6?

   3. _____

4. You toss a standard, fair die three times. What is the probability that you will toss a 6 all three times?

   4. _____

5. If an 8-ounce can of juice costs 59 cents, what is its cost per ounce?

   5. _____

6. What conversion factor can you use to change centimeters to inches?

   6. _____

7. *True or false.* $-x$ always represents a negative number.

   7. _____

8. Under a size change of -3, what are the coordinates of the image of (-1, 2)?

   8. _____

9. Maritza earns $9.75 an hour, and time and a half for overtime. What will she earn per hour of overtime?

   9. _____

10. A size change has magnitude $\frac{m}{n}$. If $m > n$, the size change is called a(n) ___?___.

    10. _____

In 11-17, simplify. Give fraction answers in lowest terms.

11. $\frac{1}{2} \cdot \frac{3}{5} =$ ___?___

    11. _____

12. $\frac{2}{3} \cdot \frac{3}{2} =$ ___?___

    12. _____

13. $2\frac{1}{2} \cdot \frac{1}{3} =$ ___?___

    13. _____

14. $-4 \cdot 2 =$ ___?___

    14. _____

15. $-6 \cdot 3.5 \cdot 10 \cdot -1 =$ ___?___

    15. _____

16. $(-5)^3 =$ ___?___

    16. _____

17. $-5 \cdot -4 \cdot -3 \cdot -2 \cdot -1 \cdot 0 =$ ___?___

    17. _____

18. A card 3" by 5" is cut along one of its diagonals. What is the area of each part?

18. _____

19. Find the volume of a box whose dimensions are 8 mm by 2.5 mm by 5 mm.

19. _____

20. 1.5 gallons • 4 $\dfrac{\text{quarts}}{\text{gallon}}$ • 2 $\dfrac{\text{pints}}{\text{quart}}$ = ____?____

20. _____

In 21-25, show your work in completing each problem.

21. Find the area of △*TRY*.

21. _____

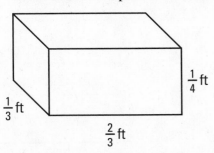

22. A metal container which holds spices is in the shape of a box whose dimensions are shown below. How many cubic *inches* of spices will the box hold?

22. _____

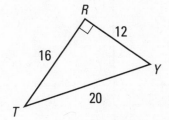

23. There are five true-false questions on your science test. If you randomly guess on each question, what is the probability you will get all five right?

23. _____

24. a. Use a rectangle to illustrate $\frac{3}{4} \cdot \frac{2}{5}$.

24. a.

   b. Give the result.

24. b. _____

25. How many inches are in a mile?

25. _____

26. $\triangle BAT$ has vertices $B = (3, 0)$, $A = (-2, 1)$, and $T = (-2, -4)$.

26. a.

   a. Draw $\triangle B'A'T'$, the image of $\triangle BAT$ under a size change of magnitude -2.

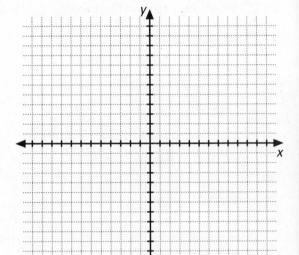

   b. $AT = 5$, so $A'T' = $ ___?___ .

b. _____

   c. Fill in the blank with $=$, $<$, or $>$:
   $m\angle B$ ___?___ $m\angle B'$

c. _____

   d. $\triangle BAT$ and $\triangle B'A'T'$ are ___?___ .

d. _____

27. Explain how the Commutative and Associative Properties of Multiplication can be used to simplify a problem like $1.8 \times 5 \times 100 \times 2$.

_____

_____

_____

Now check all your work carefully.

CHAPTER 9 TEST, Form B

1. What is the area of a rectangle 2.6 cm by 12.4 cm?

   1. _____

2. $10 \cdot (20 \cdot 30) = 10 \cdot (30 \cdot 20)$ is an instance of what property?

   2. _____

3. What is the reciprocal of 9?

   3. _____

4. You toss a standard, fair die four times. What is the probability that you will toss a 3 all four times?

   4. _____

5. If a 4-lb bunch of bananas costs $1.58, what is the cost per pound?

   5. _____

6. What conversion factor can you use to change pounds to kilograms?

   6. _____

7. *True or false.* For any nonzero number, a and $\frac{1}{a}$ are reciprocals.

   7. _____

8. Under a size change of 0.6, what are the coordinates of the image of $(-1, 2)$?

   8. _____

9. Mai earns $10.25 an hour, and time and a half for overtime. What will she make per hour of overtime?

   9. _____

10. A size change has magnitude $\frac{m}{n}$. If $m < n$, the size change is called a(n) ____?____ .

    10. _____

In 11-17, simplify. Give fraction answers in lowest terms.

11. $\frac{5}{9} \cdot \frac{1}{3} =$ ____?____

    11. _____

12. $\frac{a}{b} \cdot \frac{b}{a} =$ ____?____

    12. _____

13. $6\frac{1}{4} \cdot \frac{1}{5} =$ ____?____

    13. _____

14. $-5 \cdot 12 =$ ____?____

    14. _____

15. $-8 \cdot 4.2 \cdot 50 \cdot -2 =$ ____?____

    15. _____

16. $(-4)^4 =$ ____?____

    16. _____

17. $1 \cdot -1 \cdot 2 \cdot -2 \cdot 3 \cdot -3 =$ ____?____

    17. _____

18. A piece of cardboard 14" by 21" is cut along one of its diagonals. What is the area of each part?

18. _____

19. Find the volume of a box whose dimensions are 18 cm by 4.75 cm by 3.1 cm.

19. _____

20. 31 days • 24 $\dfrac{\text{hours}}{\text{day}}$ • 60 $\dfrac{\text{minutes}}{\text{hour}}$ = _____?_____

20. _____

In 21-25, show your work in completing each problem.

21. Find the area of $\triangle ART$.

21. _____

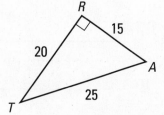

22. A container which holds water is in the shape of a box with dimensions as shown below. How many cubic meters of water will the container hold?

22. _____

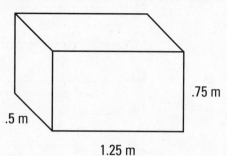

.75 m

.5 m

1.25 m

23. There are four multiple-choice questions in your science test. Each question has four choices. If you randomly guess on each question, what is the probability that you will get all wrong?

23. _____

24. a. Use a rectangle to illustrate $\frac{2}{7} \cdot \frac{1}{5}$.

24. a.

b. Give the result.

b. _____

25. To the nearest liter, how many liters are in a fish tank 60 cm by 30 cm by 36 cm?

25. _____

26. $\triangle BAT$ has vertices $B = (4, 0)$, $A = (-2, 2)$, and $T = (-2, -4)$.

26. a.

a. Draw $\triangle B'A'T'$, the image of $\triangle BAT$ under a size change of magnitude -2.5.

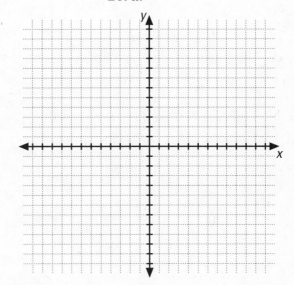

b. $AT = 6$, so $A'T' =$ ___?___.

b. _____

c. Fill in the blank with $=$, $<$, or $>$: $m\angle T$ ___?___ $m\angle T'$

c. _____

d. $\triangle BAT$ and $\triangle B'A'T'$ are ___?___.

d. _____

27. Explain how the Commutative and Associative Properties of Multiplication and the Property of Reciprocals can be used to simplify a problem like $8 \times 4 \times .125 \times .25$.

_____

_____

_____

Now check all your work carefully.

CHAPTER 9 TEST, Form C

1. Use the figure at the right to show a multiplication of two fractions. What multiplication did you show? What is the product?

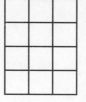

2. Suppose that the product *rst* is negative. What can you say about the numbers represented by *r, s,* and *t*? Explain your reasoning.

3. Give an example of two independent events *A* and *B* that satisfy these conditions.

   Prob (A) = 40%   *Prob (B)* = 40%

   What is *Prob (A and B)*?

4. Explain the relationship between these two conversion factors. Then give an example of the use of each.

   $$\frac{2.54 \text{ centimeters}}{1 \text{ inch}} \text{ and } \frac{1 \text{ inch}}{2.54 \text{ centimeters}}$$

5. Examine the rectangular solid below. Draw a rectangular solid of equal volume, with a different height. Be sure to label all the dimensions on your drawing.

   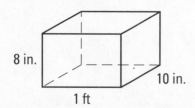

   8 in.
   10 in.
   1 ft

6. On a coordinate grid, you draw a triangle and its image under a size change of magnitude -0.5. Tell as many things as you can about the relationship between the image and the preimage.

CHAPTER 9 TEST, Form D

You have an after-school job at a garden supply store. A customer has asked for some help in planning a garden, and your boss wants you to work with the customer.

The garden will be a rectangle that is 5 yards wide and 6 yards long. The customer wants the garden divided into flower beds that are separated by paths. The paths will be 2 feet wide. There is an open section which will contain a wooden bench. At the right is the customer's rough sketch of a plan for the garden.

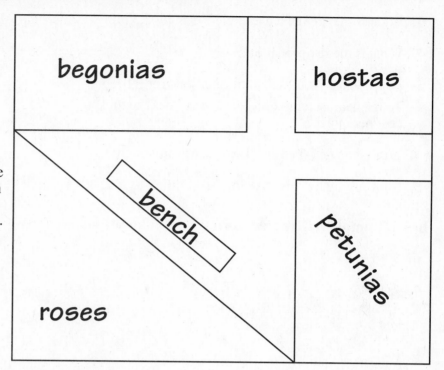

a. On graph paper, prepare an enlarged drawing of the garden that shows exact sizes for each of the flower beds. Choose an appropriate scale, and use the sketch above as a guide to help you place the flower beds. Then determine the exact dimensions of each flower bed.

b. Peat moss is used to enrich the soil. It is suggested that you place a 6-inch layer of peat moss on each flower bed, and then mix it into the soil beneath. With your plan, how many cubic feet of peat moss will be needed for the flower beds in this garden?

c. The paths and the open section are to be covered with a layer of gravel that is 2 inches deep. How many cubic feet of gravel will be needed?

d. Use the planting guide at the right. Estimate the number of plants of each type that will be needed.

Planting Guide	
For this type of plant . . .	*. . . use this spacing (approximate).*
begonia	1 plant per ft²
hosta	1 plant per 4 ft²
petunia	1 plant per 2 ft²
rose	1 bush per 2 ft²

CHAPTER 9 TEST, Cumulative Form

1. What is the area of a rectangle 3.8 m by 2.3 m?

1. _____

2. What is the reciprocal of 2.5?

2. _____

3. Suppose a $6\frac{1}{3}$-ounce can of tuna sells for 89 cents. To the nearest tenth of a cent, what does the tuna cost per ounce?

3. _____

4. *True or false.* $(-1)(x)$ is always a negative number.

4. _____

5. Multiplying by $\frac{1}{3}$ is the same as dividing by ___?___ .

5. _____

In 6-10, simplify. Give fraction answers in lowest terms.

6. $\frac{3}{8} \cdot \frac{5}{6}$

6. _____

7. $-2\frac{3}{4} \cdot \frac{1}{3}$

7. _____

8. $-6 \cdot 5.8 \cdot -1$

8. _____

9. $(-2)^4$

9. _____

10. $-6 \cdot -4 \cdot -2 \cdot 0$

10. _____

11. What is the capacity of a rectangular water trough 1 yard by 16 inches by 20 inches?

11. _____

12. What is the probability that you will get 10 heads in a row when you toss a fair coin?

12. _____

13. How many inches are in a kilometer?

13. _____

14. a. Use a rectangle to illustrate $\frac{1}{3} \cdot \frac{2}{5}$.

14. a.

    b. Give the result.

b. _____

15. $\triangle ONE$ has coordinates $O = (3, 0)$,
$N = (-2, 4)$, and $E = (2, -2)$.

    a. Draw $\triangle O'N'E'$, the image of $\triangle ONE$
    under a size change of $-\frac{1}{2}$.

15. a.

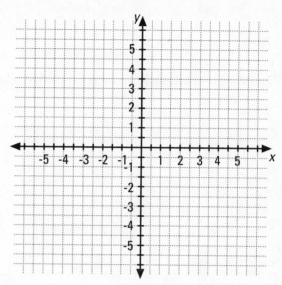

    b. Use $>$, $<$, or $=$ to make this statement
    true: $m\angle O \underline{\ \ ?\ \ } m\angle O'$

b. _____

    c. Name a point, other than O and O',
    that lies on $\overline{OO'}$.

c. _____

16. *Multiple choice.* Tell which property justifies each step.

    (a) Commutative Property of Multiplication   (b) Associative Property of Multiplication

    (c) Property of Reciprocals   (d) Multiplication Property of 1

    (e) Multiplication Property of -1   (f) Multiplication Property of 0

    $5 \cdot 6 \cdot \frac{1}{5}$

    a. $= 5 \cdot (6 \cdot \frac{1}{5})$

    b. $= 5 \cdot (\frac{1}{5} \cdot 6)$

    c. $= (5 \cdot \frac{1}{5}) \cdot 6$

    d. $= 1 \cdot 6$

    e. $= 6$

16. a. _____

b. _____

c. _____

d. _____

e. _____

In 17-20, fill in the blank.

17. *True or false.* On a coordinate graph, the point
(a, b) is always the same as the point (b, a).

17. _____

18. Draw a capital letter having only
a vertical line of symmetry.

18. _____

19. What is the perimeter of a pentagon with 3 sides of 3 cm each and the remaining sides of 2.5 cm each?

19. _____

20. ___?___ mg = 1 g

20. _____

In 21-25, write each quantity as a decimal.

21. On July 14, President Clinton requested $2.48 billion in federal relief funds for victims of the 1993 Mississippi River floods.

21. _____

22. $3\frac{1}{8}$

22. _____

23. The smallest of all free living organisms, *mycoplasma laidlawii* has a maximum diameter of 3×10^{-7} m.

23. _____

24. 60% of 125

24. _____

25. $x - y$, when $x = 5$ and $y = -7$

25. _____

26. Draw the reflection of *DRAW* over line *IT*.

26.

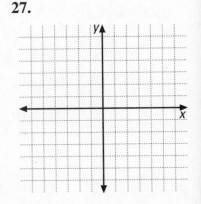

27. Graph the line $x - y = 1$.

27.

28. Use the graph below.

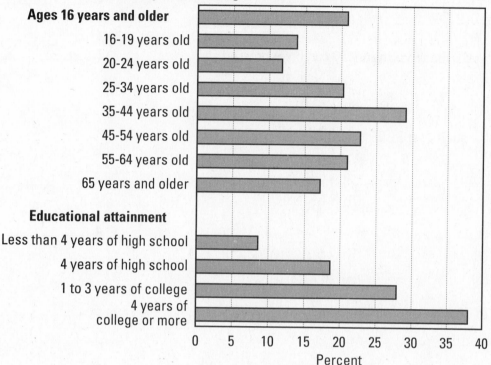

Adult Population Doing Volunteer Work in 1989

Ages 16 years and older
- 16-19 years old
- 20-24 years old
- 25-34 years old
- 35-44 years old
- 45-54 years old
- 55-64 years old
- 65 years and older

Educational attainment
- Less than 4 years of high school
- 4 years of high school
- 1 to 3 years of college
- 4 years of college or more

Percent

a. What percent of adults with 1 to 3 years of college do volunteer work?

28. a. _____

b. Which age group has the highest percent of volunteers?

b. _____

c. What is the youngest age this graph considers as adult?

c. _____

29. Solve -3.7 − *x* = 5.2. Show your work.

29. _____

30. Evaluate $15 - (3 - 7)^2/8$.

30. _____

31. Is division commutative? Explain your answer.

_____

_____

Now check all your work carefully

COMPREHENSIVE TEST, Chapters 1-9

In 1–25, *multiple choice*. Give the letter of the correct answer.

1. Which number is smallest?

    (a) $\frac{3}{10}$ (b) $\frac{4}{5}$ (c) $\frac{1}{2}$ (d) $\frac{2}{3}$

    1. _____

2. Losing $3 is worse than making $1.50 can be expressed as _____?_____ .

    (a) $3 > 1.5$ (b) $-3 < 1.5$

    (c) $-3 > 1.5$ (d) $3 < 1.5$

    2. _____

3. If peanuts in the shell cost $1.29 a pound, what will a half pound cost?

    (a) $6.50   (b) $.645

    (c) .65 cents   (d) $.65

    3. _____

4. 39.6 billion = _____?_____

    (a) 3.96×10^9 (b) 3.96×10^{10}

    (c) 3.96×10^{11} (d) 39.6×10^{10}

    4. _____

5. What power of 10 equals one million?

    (a) 3   (b) 6   (c) 9   (d) 12

    5. _____

6. How much will you pay for a $79.95 camera on sale for 30% off?

    (a) $23.985   (b) $23.99

    (c) $55.965   (d) $55.97

    6. _____

7. 4.75 kilograms = _____?_____

    (a) 4.75 g   (b) 47.5 g

    (c) 475 g   (d) 4750 g

    7. _____

8. 100 km is about

    (a) 60 miles.   (b) 70 miles.

    (c) 90 miles.   (d) 100 miles.

    8. _____

9. An appropriate U.S. unit for measuring the capacity of a bathtub is _____?_____ .

    (a) cups   (b) pints

    (c) gallons   (d) quarts

    9. _____

10. Use the formula $C = \frac{5}{9}(F - 32)$ to convert 50° F to a Celsius temperature.

    (a) -4.2°   (b) 18°

    (c) 10°   (d) 50°

    10. _____

► **COMPREHENSIVE TEST, Chapters 1-9** *page 2*

11. $15[6 - (3 + 4)2] = $ ___?___

    (a) -30   (b) -75   (c) 210   (d) -120

11. _____

12. Which means the same as $q < 0$?

    (a) q is negative.   (b) $q \leq 0$

    (c) $q > 0$ (d) $0 < q$

12. _____

13. $-15 + 32 = $ ___?___

    (a) 17   (b) -17   (c) 47   (d) -47

13. _____

14. $2\frac{2}{3} + 3\frac{3}{4} = $ ___?___

    (a) $5\frac{5}{7}$ (b) $\frac{17}{12}$ (c) $6\frac{5}{12}$ (d) $5\frac{5}{12}$

14. _____

15. In 45 minutes, the minute hand of a clock rotates

    (a) 270°.   (b) 45°.   (c) $\frac{3}{4}^{\circ}$.   (d) 90°.

15. _____

16. Which integer is a solution to $x^3 - x^2 = 448$?

    (a) 4   (b) 6   (c) 8   (d) 12

16. _____

17. There are four people in a room. Each person shakes hands with the other three people. How many handshakes are there?

    (a) 4   (b) 6   (c) 8   (d) 12

17. _____

18. If $h = 7$ and $i = -3$, then $5 - h - i = $ ___?___ .

    (a) -5   (b) -1   (c) 1   (d) 5

18. _____

19. In $\triangle WIN$, $m\angle W = m\angle I$. If $m\angle I = 52°$, $m\angle N = $ ___?___ .

    (a) 76°   (b) 138°   (c) 52°

    (d) not enough information to find $m\angle N$

19. _____

20. If $m - n = p$, then $n = $ ___?___ .

    (a) $m - p$ (b) $p - m$

    (c) $m + p$ (d) mp

20. _____

21. If (-2, 1) is reflected over the y-axis, the coordinates of the image are ___?___ .

    (a) (-2, -1)   (b) (2, 1)

    (c) (2, -1)   (d) (-2, 1)

21. _____

22. A figure with an infinite number of lines of symmetry is ___?___ .

    (a) a circle   (b) a square

    (c) a rhombus   (d) an equilateral triangle

22. _____

23. Which point is on the line $x - y = -3$?　　　　　　　　　　　23. _____

　　(a) $(6, 3)$　　　　　　　　　　(b) $(3, 6)$

　　(c) $(3, -6)$　　　　　　　　　(d) $(-6, 3)$

24. Which number cannot be a probability?　　　　　　　　　　24. _____

　　(a) 0　　　　(b) $\frac{1}{2}$　　　　(c) $-\frac{1}{2}$　　　　(d) 1

25. A figure and its size change image are always　　　　　　25. _____

　　(a) similar.　　　　　　　　　(b) congruent.

　　(c) parallel.　　　　　　　　　(d) perpendicular.

26. Graph $-3 \leq x \leq \frac{1}{2}$.　　　　　　　　　　　　**26.**

27. According to this circle graph, how many disabled　　27. _____
workers receive monthly Social-Security benefits?

Percent of Persons Receiving Monthly Social-Security Benefits, by Type of Beneficiary in 1990

Number of beneficiaries: 39,832,000

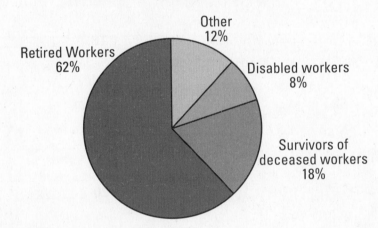

28. Convert 5 km to feet.　　　　　　　　　　　　　　　28. _____

29. There are 5 different door prizes at a party for 18 people.
Assume a person cannot win more than one prize.

　　a. What is the probability of winning a prize?　　　　29. a. _____

　　b. What is the probability of winning one of the two　　b. _____
best prizes?

30. Solve for *x*: $a - x - b = c$

30. _____

31. Which two positive integers whose product is 24 have the smallest sum?

31. _____

32. Draw a tessellation using a parallelogram as the fundamental region.

32.

33. Without using a protractor, find the indicated angle measures.

  a. m∠1

  b. m∠2

  c. m∠3

  d. m∠4

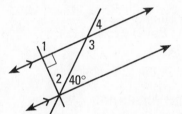

33. **a.** _____

   b. _____

   c. _____

   d. _____

34. a. Represent the sum -3.5 + 2 on this number line.

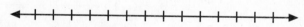

  b. Give the result.

34. **b.** _____

35. One of the heaviest humans known checked into a hospital weighing about 1387 pounds. He was discharged 16 months later weighing 476 pounds. How much did he lose?

35. _____

36. What number is the Additive Identity? What number is the Multiplicative Identity? Explain why these two numbers have these names.

_____

_____

_____

Now check all your work carefully.

1. If $f = g$, then ___?___ $= \frac{1}{2} g$.   1. _____

2. Write $4 \cdot -3$ as a repeated addition.   2. _____

3. Write a formula for the perimeter of a regular octagon with   3. _____
   sides of length n.

4. What is the reciprocal of $-\frac{1}{4}$?   4. _____

5. Simplify $3x + 2y + 9x + y$.   5. _____

In 6 and 7, solve and check. Show your work.

6. $\frac{2}{3} = \frac{5}{6} D$ 6. _____

7. $29 + 4.5K - 7 = 16$ 7. _____

In 8 and 9,
a. write an equation for each situation, and
b. answer the question.

8. A triangle is equiangular (all angles have equal measure).   8. a. _____
   Find the measure of each angle.
                                                                    b. _____

9. Star Trek Middle School has 168 science fiction books in   9. a. _____
   the school library. If this is 1.9% of all the books in the
   library, find the total number of books in the collection.   b. _____

Name

QUIZ

1. The Distributive Property involves addition and what other operation?

1. _____

2. How many faces does a rectangular solid have?

2. _____

In 3 and 4, solve and check. Show your work.

3. $-5\frac{1}{8}M = 32$

3. _____

4. $-14.5 + 3.8L + 7.75 - 6.3L = 43.25$

4. _____

In 5 and 6, simplify. There should be no parentheses in your final answer.

5. $8\frac{1}{2} \cdot 7 + 1\frac{1}{2} \cdot 7$

5. _____

6. $6(x + y) + 2.5(x + 2y)$

6. _____

7. Find the surface area of the rectangular solid below.

7. _____

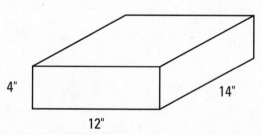

4"

14"

12"

8. Use rectangles to show that
$1x + 2x + 3x + 4x = (1 + 2 + 3 + 4)x$.

8. _____

CHAPTER 10 TEST, Form A

1. Simplify $k + k + k + k + 2j + 2j + 2j$.

   1. _____

2. If $a = b$, then $5a = $ ___?___ .

   2. _____

3. Write $\frac{1}{2} + \frac{1}{2} + \frac{1}{2} + \frac{1}{2} + \frac{1}{2} + \frac{1}{2}$ as a multiplication.

   3. _____

4. Simplify $x(y + 7) - xy$.

   4. _____

5. To solve $-4x = 3.2$, multiply both sides by ___?___ .

   5. _____

6. The perimeter of a garden is measured in feet. What unit would be used to measure the area of the garden?

   6. _____

7. Find the area of $\triangle AGE$ below.

   7. _____

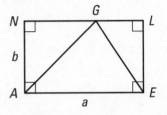

In 8-10, refer to the hexagon pictured below.

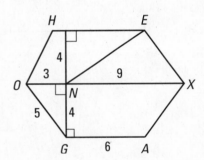

8. Find the area of triangle NGO.

   8. _____

9. Find the area of triangle EXN.

   9. _____

10. Find the area of trapezoid $XAGO$.

    10. _____

► **CHAPTER 10 TEST, Form A** *page 2*

In 11-14, solve. Show your work.

11. $-.432x = -95.04$

11. _____

12. $1\frac{4}{7}t = \frac{2}{5}$

12. _____

13. $32 + \frac{9}{5}C = 212$

13. _____

14. $6y - 7 - 13y + 21 = 0$

14. _____

15. In 1993, Chicago's Amoco Building was ranked the world's fourth tallest building. The structure is roughly a rectangular solid with a square base 185 ft on a side and a volume of 38,880,000 ft³.

a. What is the area of the base of the building?

15. a. _____

b. To the nearest foot, find the building's height.

b. _____

c. In what unit would the building's exterior surface area most probably be measured?

c. _____

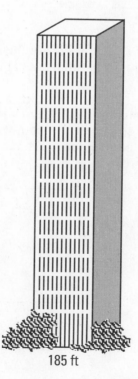

185 ft

16. The balance scale diagram below represents what equation?

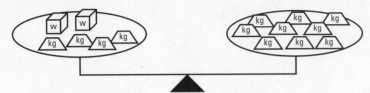

16. _____

17. Show how to use the Distributive Property to calculate $11.98 × 4. The product should be the last line in your work.

17. _____

18. What instance of the Distributive Property is pictured here?

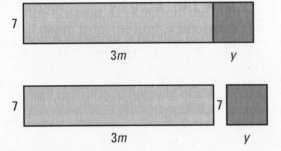

18. _____

19. A family paid $6,750 in taxes. This is 22% of their yearly income. Rounded to the nearest ten dollars, what is their yearly income?

19. _____

20. Suppose a gift box is 30.48 cm long, 20.32 cm wide, and 5.08 cm high. To the nearest square centimeter, what is the least area of wrapping paper needed to wrap the gift?

20. _____

21. Tell how you know that the area of trapezoid *TRAP* is equal to the sum of the areas of triangles *TRA* and *TAP*.

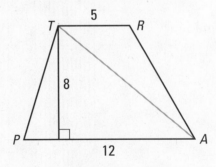

_____

_____

Now check all your work carefully.

Name _____

CHAPTER 10 TEST, Form B

1. Simplify $d - 6d + a + a + a + b + b$.

    1. _____

2. If $a = b$, then $7.34a =$ ___?___ .

    2. _____

3. Write $\frac{2}{5} + \frac{2}{5} + \frac{2}{5} + \frac{2}{5} + \frac{2}{5} + \frac{2}{5}$ as a multiplication.

    3. _____

4. Simplify $(3a - 4b)b + 4b^2$.

    4. _____

5. To solve $-7.2x = 14.4$, multiply both sides by ___?___ .

    5. _____

6. If the radius of the earth is measured in miles, in what unit would the surface area of the earth most likely be measured?

    6. _____

7. Find the area of $\triangle AGE$ below.

    7. _____

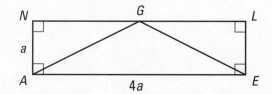

In 8-10, refer to the hexagon pictured below.

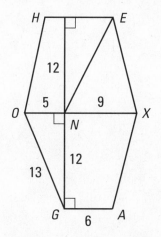

8. Find the area of triangle NGO.

    8. _____

9. Find the area of triangle EXN.

    9. _____

10. Find the area of trapezoid $XAGO$.

    10. _____

Name

In 11-14, solve. Show your work.

11. $-23.27z = 395.59$ 11. _____

12. $2\frac{3}{4}M = \frac{1}{3}$ 12. _____

13. $\frac{5}{9}F - 17\frac{7}{9} = 37$ 13. _____

14. $-8y + 36 + 17y - 7 = 2$ 14. _____

15. A custom-made fish tank has a square base
50 cm on a side. It holds 100 liters (100,000 cm³)
of water.

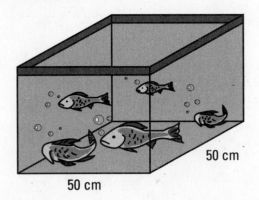

50 cm

50 cm

a. What is the area of the base of the fish tank?   15. a. _____

b. To the nearest cm, find the fish tank's height.   b. _____

c. In what unit would the fish tank's exterior surface area
most probably be measured?   c. _____

Name _____

16. The balance scale diagram below represents   16. _____
what equation?

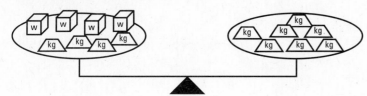

17. Show how to use the Distributive Property to calculate   17. _____
$9.98 × 5. The product should be the last line in
your work.

18. Use rectangles to show that   18. _____
$5.2x + 10.4x = (5.2 + 10.4)x$.

19. The Mehta family has completed 67 miles of a 132-mile   19. _____
car trip. If their average speed is 50 miles per hour, how
long will it take them to reach their destination?

20. Will a single sheet of newspaper which measures   20. _____
$27\frac{1}{4}$" by $22\frac{1}{2}$" be enough to wrap a box
which is a foot long, a foot wide, and half a foot high?   _____
Why or why not?

21. Tell how you know that the area of trapezoid *TRAP* is
equal to the sum of the areas of triangles *TRA* and *TAP*.

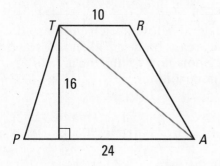

_____

_____

Now check all your work carefully.

CHAPTER 10 TEST, Form C

1. Which of the following equations have the same solution as $-8t = 2$? Tell how you know.

$$-8t = -2 \qquad -2t = 8$$
$$8t = -2 \qquad -4t = 1$$

2. Make up a real-life problem that you can solve with this equation:

$$5n + 128 = 340.50$$

Use the equation to solve your problem.

3. Make a drawing that shows how areas of rectangles illustrate the Distributive Property.

4. Alana simplified the expression $8k - k$ and said that the answer is 8. Explain why her answer is incorrect.

5. The rectangular solid shown below is a small box. Suppose its length, width, and height are each doubled. Would you need twice as much cardboard to construct the new box? Explain your reasoning.

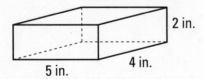

6. On the grid below, sketch a trapezoid whose area is between 40 and 50 square units. Show how to find the area of your trapezoid.

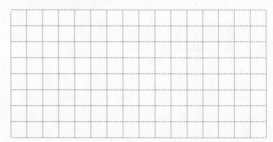

CHAPTER 10 TEST, Form D

You and your friends have created a new snack mix. Your classmates love the mix, and they are encouraging you to package and sell it at the Spring Fair. Now it is your job to plan an attractive box for the mix.

At the right is a sketch of a net for a snack-food box.

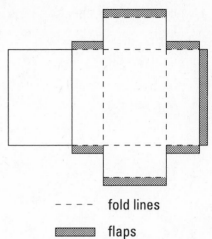

- - - - fold lines

▨▨▨▨ flaps

a. When the net is folded into a three-dimensional shape, the flaps will tuck under the faces of the box and will no longer be visible. How many faces will the box have? What is the geometric name of the three-dimensional shape that is formed?

b. One ounce of your snack mix occupies a little less than 6 cubic inches of space. Suppose that you want to sell the mix in one-pound boxes. How many cubic inches of space must your box enclose?

c. Use your answer to the question in Part b to plan reasonable dimensions (length, width, height) for your box.

d. Draw a net for your box on a separate sheet of paper, using the figure above as a model. Be sure to choose a reasonable size for each flap and include the flaps in the net. Then label each part of the net with its exact dimensions.

e. How much cardboard is needed for your box?

f. Suppose that your teacher can provide rectangular sheets of cardboard that are 3 feet long and 2 feet wide. How many boxes could you make from one sheet of this cardboard? How much of each sheet would be wasted?

CHAPTER 10 TEST, Cumulative Form

In 1-5, solve and check.

1. $\frac{1}{2}y + 5 = 77$

   1. _____

2. $-52 = 13m$

   2. _____

3. $17 - 3t + 9 = -70.$

   3. _____

4. Solve $mn = p$ for m.

   4. _____

5. $15 - 4y = 85$

   5. _____

In 6-11, simplify.

6. $2a + b + 2a + b + b$

   6. _____

7. $3 \cdot \frac{m}{9}$

   7. _____

8. $9x + -13x$

   8. _____

9. $8(20 + t + n)$

   9. _____

10. $-\frac{3}{4} \cdot 16$

    10. _____

11. $-40 \cdot -y \cdot -2$

    11. _____

12. Write $\frac{7}{18}$ as a decimal.

    12. _____

13. Find the area of $\triangle XYZ$.

    13. _____

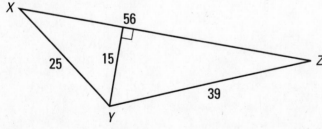

14. If 42% of *b* books are used, how many books are new?   14. _____

15. Find the area of the shaded region.   15. _____

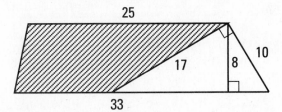

**In 16 and 17, consider a rectangular box with no lid that is
30 cm long, 15 cm wide, and 20 cm high.**

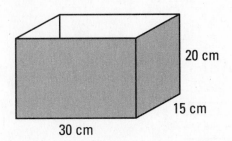

16. What is the outside surface area?   16. _____

17. What is the volume of the box?   17. _____

18. In general, how many dimensions are needed to
measure area?   18. _____

19. In general, how many dimensions are needed to
measure volume?   19. _____

20. Tell whether each measure listed is used for length,
volume, or weight.

　　a. liter   20. a. _____

　　b. gram   b. _____

　　c. cubic centimeter   c. _____

21. Sketch two rectangular boxes that have the same
volume but different surface areas. Label all
necessary dimensions.   **21.**

22. In a size change of $\triangle ABC$ when $A = (-2, 5)$, $B = (6, 6)$, and $C = (5, 3)$, two image points are $A' = (1, -2.5)$ and $B' = (-3, -3)$. Find the coordinates of C', the image of C.

22. _____

23. What is the magnitude of the size change in Question 22?

23. _____

24. If there is a 50% chance of rain today in Tokyo and a 70% chance of rain today in London, what are the chances that it will rain in both cities today ?

24. _____

25. Multiply: $200 \text{ cars} \cdot 3 \dfrac{\text{passengers}}{\text{car}} \cdot \dfrac{\$1.25}{\text{passenger}}$

25. _____

26. Is a distance of 50 km longer or shorter than 32 miles?

26. _____

27. What is 83% of 40?

27. _____

28. Round π^2 to the nearest thousandth.

28. _____

In 29 and 30, use the graph below.

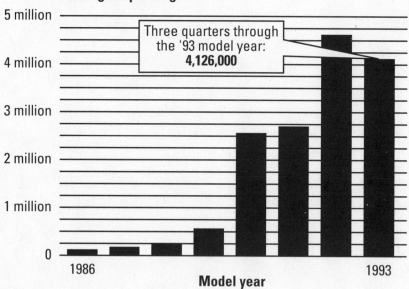

29. If the 1993 rate continued through that model year, about how many cars manufactured in the 1993 model year had air bags by the end of the year?

29. _____

30. About how large was the increase between 1989 and 1990?

30. _____

Now check all your work carefully.

QUIZ

In 1-4, simplify.

1. $\dfrac{\frac{3}{5}}{\frac{3}{10}}$

1. _____

2. $-16 \div -2$

2. _____

3. $\dfrac{-6\frac{2}{3}}{1\frac{2}{3}}$

3. _____

4. $\dfrac{12}{-\frac{4}{7}}$

4. _____

5. Tell whether $-\dfrac{m}{n}$ is positive or negative when $m = -2$ and $n = 5$.

5. _____

6. Use the Quotient-Remainder Formula to write an equation relating the divisor, dividend, quotient, and remainder in this division.

   $$15\overline{)79} \quad 5\,R4$$

6. _____

7. You watched h hours of TV in d days. On the average, how many hours did you watch per day?

7. _____

In 8-9, show your work.

8. The tallest mountain in Mexico is Citlaltepetl, which is 18,700 feet above sea level. How tall is this in miles and feet?

8. _____

9. Store A has organic tomatoes for sale at 5 lb for \$6.45. Store B has the same tomatoes for sale at 3 lb for \$3.36. Which store has the cheaper tomatoes? Justify your answer.

9. _____

Name _____

QUIZ

1. Compare the number of students at Jefferson Middle School, 329, and the number at Lincoln Middle School, 412, in two ways.

   1. _____

   _____

2. To get rid of fractions in the equation $\frac{3}{t} = \frac{10}{17}$, by what can you multiply both sides?

   2. _____

3. According to the Means-Extremes Property, what must be true if $\frac{K}{L} = \frac{M}{N}$?

   3. _____

4. *Multiple choice.* Which is *not* a proportion?

   (a) $\frac{3+x}{4} = \frac{2}{3}$ (b) $3 + \frac{x}{4} = \frac{2}{3}$

   (c) $\frac{3x}{4} = \frac{2}{3}$ (d) All are proportions.

   4. _____

5. A rectangle has length 8 cm and width 3 cm. A similar rectangle has length 12 cm. What is its width?

   5. _____

In 6 and 7, solve.

6. $\frac{4}{x} = \frac{18}{26}$

   6. _____

7. $\frac{3.2}{5} = \frac{8}{y}$

   7. _____

8. Juanita earned $5.89 interest on savings of $155. What percent interest did she earn?

   8. _____

9. Given these two similar triangles, find the perimeter of $\triangle TOP$.

   9. _____

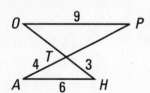

CHAPTER 11 TEST, Form A

1. Use the Quotient-Remainder Formula to write an
   equation relating these numbers: When 31 is divided by
   7, the result is 4 with a remainder of 3.

   1. _____

2. If a fish market charges d dollars to smoke p pounds of
   salmon, what is the cost per pound to smoke salmon?

   2. _____

3. Rewrite $\frac{1}{2} \div \frac{3}{4}$ as a multiplication problem.

   3. _____

4. *Multiple choice.* Which of the following is *not* equal to
   the other three?

   (a) $\frac{-7}{2}$ (b) $\frac{7}{-2}$

   (c) $\frac{-7}{-2}$ (d) $-\frac{7}{2}$

   4. _____

5. 10 is what percent of 5?

   5. _____

6. By what can you multiply both sides of this
   equation to eliminate the fractions: $\frac{t}{6} = \frac{7}{11}$?

   6. _____

7. In $\frac{t}{6} = \frac{7}{11}$, which numbers are the extremes?

   7. _____

8. The sides of a triangle with sides 4 cm, 5 cm, and 6 cm
   are reduced to 50% of their original size. What are the
   lengths of the sides of the new triangle?

   8. _____

**For 9 and 10, use these populations for the most and least
populous states in 1992:
California's population was 30,866,851, and
Wyoming's population was 466,185.**

9. California's population was about ___?___ times that of
   Wyoming. Round to the nearest tenth.

   9. _____

10. Wyoming's population was about ___?___ percent that of
    California. Round to the nearest tenth of a percent.

    10. _____

11. What is the relationship between the exact answers in
    Questions 9 and 10? Explain why this relationship exists.

    _____

    _____

    _____

Name _____

In 12-16, simplify or solve.

12. $\dfrac{\frac{3}{5}}{\frac{1}{2}}$

12. _____

13. $\dfrac{4\frac{2}{3}}{6\frac{3}{4}}$

13. _____

14. $\dfrac{-6}{4}$

14. _____

15. $\dfrac{-3.5}{-1.4}$

15. _____

16. $\dfrac{a}{10} = \dfrac{12}{25}$

16. _____

In 17-20, show your work.

17. One of the largest watches ever made was 787.5 inches in diameter. How many feet and inches is this?

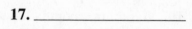 17. _____

18. In fiscal year 1991, the 28,912 post offices in the U.S. handled 165.851 billion letters and packages. What was the average number of pieces of mail handled per post office in 1991?

 18. _____

19. In 1991, Chrysler Corporation spent about $530 million on advertising and earned about $29.4 billion from sales. That same year Ford Motor Company spent about $675 million on advertising and earned about $89 billion from sales. Which car company earned more per advertising dollar? Justify your answer.

20. If it took a teacher $\frac{1}{3}$ of an hour to grade four tests, how long will it take the teacher to grade 26 tests?

21. Quadrilaterals *ABCD* and *EFGH* are similar with corresponding sides parallel.

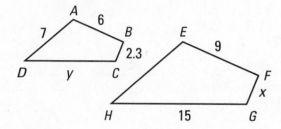

    a. Find *x*.

    b. Find *y*.

21. a. _____

    b. _____

22. Write a problem that could lead to dividing -15 by -5.

_____

_____

_____

Now check all your work carefully.

CHAPTER 11 TEST, Form B

1. Use the Quotient-Remainder Formula to write an equation relating all these numbers: when 67 is divided by 9, the result is 7 with a remainder of 4.

   1. _____

2. If a grocery store charges $12.50 for p pounds of coffee, what is the cost per pound?

   2. _____

3. Rewrite $\frac{2}{3} \div \frac{1}{4}$ as a multiplication problem.

   3. _____

4. *Multiple choice.* Which of the following is *not* equal to the other three?

   (a) $\frac{-5}{-9}$ (b) $-\frac{5}{9}$

   (c) $\frac{-5}{9}$ (d) $\frac{5}{-9}$

   4. _____

5. 16 is what percent of 4?

   5. _____

6. By what can you multiply both sides of this equation to eliminate the fractions: $\frac{5}{3} = \frac{12}{x}$?

   6. _____

7. In $\frac{5}{3} = \frac{12}{x}$, which numbers are the extremes?

   7. _____

8. The sides of a triangle whose lengths are 12 cm, 16 cm, and 20 cm are reduced to 50% of their original size. What are the lengths of the sides of the new triangle?

   8. _____

For 9 and 10, use these areas for the most and least populous states:
California has an area of 158,706 square miles while Wyoming's area is 97,809 square miles.

9. California's area is about ___?___ times that of Wyoming. Round to the nearest tenth.

   9. _____

10. Wyoming's area is about ___?___ percent that of California. Round to the nearest tenth of a percent.

    10. _____

11. What is the relationship between the exact answers in Questions 9 and 10? Explain why this relationship exists.

   _____

   _____

   _____

In 12-16, simplify or solve.

12. $\dfrac{\frac{2}{9}}{\frac{4}{3}}$ 12. _____

13. $\dfrac{5\frac{1}{2}}{2\frac{5}{8}}$ 13. _____

14. $\dfrac{18}{-12}$ 14. _____

15. $\dfrac{-7.6}{-11.4}$ 15. _____

16. $\dfrac{b}{14} = \dfrac{12.5}{35}$ 16. _____

In 17-20, show your work.   17. _____

17. The length of an Olympic size pool is about 1968.5
    inches. How many feet and inches is this?

18. In 1993 there were approximately 917 million $2 bills in   18. _____
    circulation. If the 1993 U.S. population was about
    249 million, approximately how many $2 bills were there
    per person?

19. In 1991, Pepsico (the makers of Pepsi) spent about $900 million on advertising and earned about $19.8 billion from sales. That same year Coca-Cola spent about $370 million on advertising and earned $11.6 billion from sales. Which company earned more per advertising dollar? Justify your answer.

19. _____

20. If it takes a window washer 20 minutes to wash five windows, how long would it take her to wash 127 windows?

20. _____

21. Quadilaterals *ABCD* and *EFGH* are similar with corresponding sides parallel.

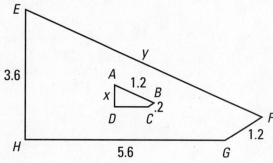

   a. Find *x*.

   b. Find *y*.

21. a. _____

    b. _____

22. Write a problem that could lead to dividing 30 by -6.

   _____

   _____

   _____

Now check all your work carefully.

CHAPTER 11 TEST, Form C

1. The segment below is $5\frac{1}{2}$ units long. To divide it into 3 parts of equal length, what division should you do? Show how to find the quotient on the diagram.

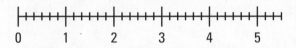

Find the quotient using the algebraic definition of division.

2. Describe two situations that can be represented by this division.

$$5 \div 7$$

One situation should involve rates, and the other should involve ratios.

3. The mean of a set of five temperatures is negative. Must all the temperatures in the set be negative? Give an example to support your answer.

4. Tom earns $25 for working 4 hours. To find the amount he would earn in working 18 hours, he wrote this proportion.

$$\frac{25}{4} = \frac{18}{n}$$

Explain why Tom's proportion is incorrect. Then write a correct proportion and use it to solve the problem.

5. Copy rectangle *ABCD* onto a sheet of graph paper. Then draw a rectangle *WXYZ* that is similar to *ABCD*. Explain why the rectangles are similar.

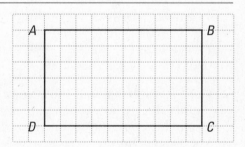

CHAPTER 11 TEST, Form D

You are thinking of getting a part-time job. Your parents say that they will agree with your choice of a job, provided that you do some planning. They want you to think ahead about how much money you will earn and how you will use it.

At the right are the jobs that were posted on the school bulletin board.

a. Suppose you take the job at the Boys' and Girls' Club. How many hours would you have to work in order to earn $100?

b. In which job would you earn the most for one hour of work?

c. Choose one job—or a combination of jobs—that you think you would like. Determine how much you would earn from the job or jobs in one *year*.

d. Think about how you would use the money you earned from the job or jobs that you chose in Part c. For example, here are some categories that other students have listed.

entertainment	sports	food
transportation	hobbies	clothing
school supplies	savings	gifts

List the categories in which you plan to use the money you earn. Then make a budget for the coming year that shows how much of your total earnings you plan to use in each of your categories. What percent of the total is in each category?

e. Make a graph that will show your parents clearly how much you plan to earn in the coming year and how you will use the money.

$ Jobs $ Jobs $ Jobs $

Parents' Helper
M – F afternoons
4:00 – 6:00
$28.75/week
Call 555-0041.

WALK MY DOG!
(She's a real cutie, and she walks fast.)
about 1 hour a day
7 days a week
$25/week
Call 555-6135.

Distribute Advertising Flyers!
Saturdays
8:00 A.M. – 12:00 N.
$15
Call 555-4829.

Reader for Blind Student
Sept. – June
MTTh afternoons
3:30 – 6:00
$14/day
Call 555-2416.

Boys' and Girls' Club
Sports Assistant
M – F afternoons
3:30 – 5:30
$6.75/day
Call 555-0008.

Baby-sitter
Sat. evenings
6:00 – 10:00
$12
Call 555-9278.

Newspaper Carrier Mornings
$20/week (7 days, about 1 hour daily)
Deliver papers to 25 homes in Midtown area.
Call 555-NEWS.

Lawn Care
March through October
Mowing, Weeding, Trimming
5 hours per week
$25 per week
Call 555-2416.

CHAPTER 11 TEST, Cumulative Form

1. If r oranges produce c cups of juice, what expression represents the amount of juice per orange?

1. _____

2. Rewrite $3 \div \frac{1}{2}$ as a multiplication problem.

2. _____

3. 20 is what percent of 16?

3. _____

4. By what can you multiply both sides of this equation to eliminate the fractions: $\frac{5}{m} = \frac{18}{11}$?

4. _____

5. *Multiple choice.* Which is *not* equal to the other three?

   (a) $\frac{-2}{-3}$ (b) $\frac{-2}{3}$ (c) $\frac{2}{-3}$ (d) $-\frac{2}{3}$

5. _____

6. In 1992, the per capita income of Mississippi was $14,088. The same year in New Jersey, it was $26,457. To the nearest tenth of a percent, Mississippi's average income was what percent of New Jersey's average income?

6. _____

In 7-10, simplify.

7. $\dfrac{\frac{2}{3}}{\frac{5}{6}}$

7. _____

8. $\dfrac{7\frac{1}{2}}{2\frac{2}{5}}$

8. _____

9. $\frac{-8}{5}$

9. _____

10. $\frac{-2.4}{-.6}$

10. _____

In 11 and 12, solve each proportion.

11. $\frac{6}{s} = \frac{12}{22}$

11. _____

12. $\frac{5}{24} = \frac{T}{36}$

12. _____

13. In baseball, the distance from home plate to second base is about 1527 inches. How far is this in feet and inches?

13. _____

14. In 1982, H. Ross Perot, Jr., set a world record for the fastest helicopter trip around the world. If he flew about 24,000 miles in about 29 days, what was his average speed in miles per hour?

14. _____

15. Write a problem that could lead to dividing -10 by -5.

15. _____

16. If 68 grams of cherries (about 10 cherries) have   16. _____
45 calories of food energy, how many calories do
95.2 grams of cherries have?

17. Simplify $6p - 2p - 4q + p$.   17. _____

18. Write without parentheses: $x(3 + y)$ 18. _____

19. *Multiple choice.* A figure with at least one pair of parallel   19. _____
sides is called

   (a) a trapezoid.   (b) a parallelogram.

   (c) a rectangle.   (d) all of the above.

20. A triangle with area 10 square feet has a base of 5 feet.   20. _____
What is the height of the triangle?

21. A bag contains slips of paper labeled with the numbers 1   21. _____
through 15. What is the probability that you will choose a
slip with a number divisible by 2 or by 3?

22. Evaluate -2 − 6 − -10.   22. _____

23. How many meters are in 10 km?   23. _____

24. 246 million ft³ of material was excavated to build the   24. _____
tunnel under the English Channel. Write this number in
scientific notation.

25. For the rectangular solid
pictured, find

   a. the surface area.   25. a. _____

   b. the volume.   b. _____

26. Solve: $6x - 8 = -4$ 26. _____

27. Show how to use the Distributive Property to find   27. _____
99 • 54 mentally.

_____

28. The government suggests spending about 25% of your   28. _____
income on housing. If a family earns $22,500 a year, how
much could they spend on housing?

29. Evaluate $\dfrac{12 - 2(4 - 2)^2}{5 - 1}$.   29. _____

30. Graph $-2.5 < a \le 3$ on this number line.   30.

   ◀——┼┼┼┼┼┼┼┼┼┼┼┼┼┼┼┼┼——▶

Now check all your work carefully.

Name _____

1. Write 6.2 as a simple fraction.   1. _____

2. *Multiple choice.* Which of the following is *not* equal to a   2. _____
    terminating decimal?

    (a) $\frac{1}{2}$ (b) $\frac{1}{3}$ (c) $\frac{1}{4}$ (d) $\frac{1}{5}$

3. What is the symbol $\sqrt{}$ called?   3. _____

4. Round $\sqrt{75}$ to the nearest tenth.   4. _____

5. The longest side of a right triangle is called its __?__.   5. _____

6. *True or false.* The Pythagorean Theorem works for   6. _____
    any triangle.

7. Write $.\overline{72}$ as a fraction in lowest terms.   7. _____

In 8-10, evaluate. Do not use a calcuator.

8. $\sqrt{6^2} + \sqrt{8^2}$ 8. _____

9. $\sqrt{6^2 + 8^2}$ 9. _____

10. $\sqrt{\sqrt{81}}$ 10. _____

In 11 and 12, show your work.

11. A baseball "diamond" is really a square. If it is 90 ft from   11. _____
    first base to second base, how far is the throw from
    second base to home plate?

12. A 15-foot pole is to be steadied by   12. _____
    wires from the top of the pole to the
    ground. These wires are 17 feet
    long. How far from the base of the
    pole will the wires attach to
    the ground?

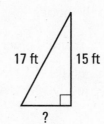

17 ft   15 ft

?

QUIZ

1. Write a formula for the circumference C of a circle in terms of its radius r.

   1. _____

2. *True or false.* All irrational numbers are real numbers.

   2. _____

3. *Multiple choice.* The number π

   (a) is exactly equal to 3.14.

   (b) is exactly equal to $\frac{22}{7}$.

   (c) cannot be written as a decimal or fraction.

   3. _____

4. A sector of a circle has a central angle with measure of 120°. Its area is what fraction of the area of the circle?

   4. _____

In 5 and 6, tell whether the quantity is a surface area or a volume.

5. the amount of paper used for a soup-can label

   5. _____

6. the amount of soup in a can

   6. _____

7. For the cylinder at the right, find each measure.

   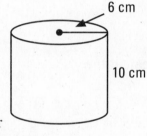

   6 cm

   10 cm

   a. its lateral area to the nearest square centimeter

   7. a. _____

   b. its total surface area to the nearest square centimeter

   b. _____

   c. its volume to the nearest 10 cubic centimeters

   c. _____

8. Draw a net for the triangular prism pictured below.

   8.

   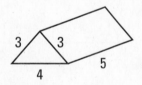

   3   3

   4   5

In 9-11, a circular pool is 25 feet in diameter and 3 feet deep.

9. What is the circumference of the pool?

   9. _____

10. The bottom of the pool is to be painted blue. How much area needs to be painted?

    10. _____

11. How much water can the pool hold?

    11. _____

CHAPTER 12 TEST, Form A

These formulas may help you with this test.

Pythagorean Theorem	$a^2 + b^2 = c^2$
Circumference of a circle	$C = \pi d$
Area of a circle	$A = \pi r^2$
Volume of a cylindric solid	$V = hB$
Surface area of a sphere	$S = 4\pi r^2$
Volume of a sphere	$V = \frac{4}{3}\pi r^3$

1. *Multiple choice.* Which number is irrational?   1. _____

    (a) $\sqrt{4}$ (b) $\sqrt{8}$

    (c) $\sqrt{16}$ (d) $\sqrt{64}$

2. Between which two consecutive integers is $\sqrt{70}$?   2. _____

3. Name the two square roots of 25.   3. _____

4. A square has area 60 cm². Give the exact length of a side   4. _____
of the square.

5. Write a formula relating the radius r of a circle to the   5. _____
diameter d of the circle.

6. A sector of a circle has a central angle of 60°. The area of   6. _____
the sector is what fraction of the area of the circle?

7. The Pythagorean Theorem applies to what type   7. _____
of figures?

**In 8 -10, find a simple fraction in lowest terms equal to the
given number.**

8. -5.75   8. _____

9. $0.0\overline{7}$ 9. _____

10. $6.\overline{48}$ 10. _____

Name _____

In 11 and 12, find the missing length. Give an exact answer.

11.

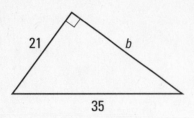

11. _____

12.

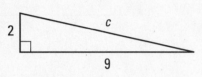

12. _____

13. A square block is 220 feet on a side. You need to go from one corner of the block to the opposite corner. How many feet less is the trip along the diagonal of the square than along two of the sides? Give your answer to the nearest foot.

13. _____

14. A quarter has a diameter of approximately 23mm. What is its circumference, to the nearest millimeter?

14. _____

In 15 and 16, use this information: PIZZA-PIES-TO-GO offers three sizes of pizza:
    A small pizza with a 3.5" radius
    A medium pizza with a 6" radius
    A large pizza with an 8" radius

15. Fiona ordered 5 small pizzas and Leon ordered one large pizza.

a. Who ordered more pizza?

15. a. _____

b. Explain your answer to Part a.

_____

_____

16. Leon ate 3 of the 12 equal-sized slices of his large pizza. How many square inches of pizza did he eat? Give your answer to the nearest square inch.

16. _____

Name _____

In 17 and 18, use the triangular prism shown below.

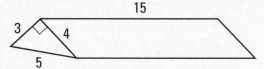

17. Calculate its lateral area.

17. _____

18. Calculate its volume.

18. _____

In 19 and 20, use this information: The Three Rivers water tunnel in Atlanta, Georgia, is the largest machine-bored tunnel in the world. It is 30,769 feet long, and has a diameter of 10.5 feet.

19. a. Would you include the two bases when calculating the surface area of this tunnel? Why or why not?

19. a. _____

_____

_____

b. Determine the surface area of the tunnel, to the nearest 10,000 square feet.

b. _____

20. Determine the volume of this tunnel to the nearest 10,000 cubic feet.

20. _____

In 21 and 22, use this information: The world's largest planetarium is in Miyazaki, Japan. The dome has a radius of about 44 feet.

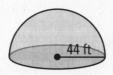

21. If the planetarium's dome is a perfect hemisphere (half sphere), give its volume, to the nearest 1,000 cubic feet.

21. _____

22. What is the surface area of the dome?

22. _____

Now check all your work carefully.

CHAPTER 12 TEST, Form B

These formulas may help you with this test.

Pythagorean Theorem	$a^2 + b^2 = c^2$
Circumference of a circle	$C = \pi d$
Area of a circle	$A = \pi r^2$
Volume of a cylindric solid	$V = hB$
Surface area of a sphere	$S = 4\pi r^2$
Volume of a sphere	$V = \frac{4}{3}\pi r^3$

1. *Multiple choice.* Which number is irrational?　　　　　1. _____

    (a) $\sqrt{19}$　　　　　　　　(b) $\sqrt{9}$

    (c) $\sqrt{25}$　　　　　　　　(d) $\sqrt{121}$

2. Between which two consecutive integers is $\sqrt{105}$?　　2. _____

3. Name the two square roots of 49.　　　　　　　　　3. _____

4. A square has area 14 cm². Give the exact length of a side　4. _____
   of the square.

5. Write a formula relating the radius r of a circle to the　　5. _____
   circumference C of the circle.

6. A sector of a circle has a central angle of 120°. The area　6. _____
   of the sector is what fraction of the area of the circle?

7. *True or false.* The Pythagorean Theorem applies to　　7. _____
   all triangles.

In 8-10, find a simple fraction in lowest terms equal to the given number.

8. -4.25　　　　　　　　　　　　　　　　　　　　8. _____

9. $0.00\overline{2}$　　　　　　　　　　　　　　　　　　　9. _____

10. $8.\overline{12}$　　　　　　　　　　　　　　　　　　　10. _____

Name _____

In 11 and 12, find the missing length. Give an exact answer.

11.

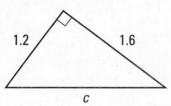

11. _____

12.

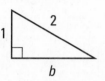

12. _____

13. The maker of a thermometer wanted to design a carrying case the size of a credit card for the thermometer. If the thermometer is 91 mm long, will it fit along the diagonal of a credit card which is 85 mm long and 54 mm wide? Justify your answer.

13. _____

   _____

   _____

   _____

14. A dime has a radius of approximately 9 mm. What is its circumference, to the nearest millimeter?

14. _____

In 15 and 16, use this information: In one year, the earth completes its orbit around the sun. This orbit is nearly a circle with the sun at the center. The distance from the earth to the sun is about 93 million miles.

15. a. To the nearest 10 million miles, what distance does the earth travel in one year?

15. a. _____

   b. What is the area of the circle?

   b. _____

16. In one day, the earth's orbit forms a sector with a central angle of about 1°. What is the approximate area of the sector formed in one week?

16. _____

In 17 and 18, use the triangular prism shown below.

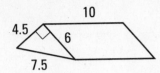

17. Calculate its lateral area.

17. _____

18. Calculate its volume.

18. _____

In 19 and 20, use this information: The Alaska pipeline carries oil from Prudhoe Bay to Valdez. It is 800 miles long and has a diameter of 4 feet.

19. **a.** Would you include the two bases when calculating the surface area of the pipeline? Why or why not?

19. a. _____

_____

_____

   b. Determine the surface area of the pipeline, to the nearest 10,000 square feet.

b. _____

20. Determine the volume of this pipeline to the nearest 10,000 cubic feet.

20. _____

In 21 and 22, use this information: An orange with a $2\frac{1}{4}''$ radius is cut into four equal-sized wedges.

21. Find the volume of each wedge to the nearest 0.1 in.^{3}

21. _____

22. Find the surface area of the peel on each wedge, to the nearest 0.1 in.^{2}

22. _____

Now check all your work carefully.

CHAPTER 12 TEST, Form C

1. How do you know that $\sqrt{55}$ is close to 7.4?

2. Use three of the lengths 40 mm, 42 mm, 50 mm, and 58 mm to draw a right triangle. Then use three of the lengths to draw a triangle that is *not* a right triangle. Describe the relationship that exists between the sides of the right triangle you drew.

3. Danny used this method to find a simple fraction equal to $0.4\overline{09}$.

$$x = 0.4\overline{09}$$
$$10x = 4.\overline{09}$$
$$10x - x = 4.\overline{09} - 0.4\overline{09}$$
$$9x = 4 - 0.04 = 3.6$$
$$x = \frac{3.6}{9} = \frac{36}{90} = \frac{2}{5}$$

Find the error(s) in Danny's method. Then show a correct way to find the fraction.

4. The figure at the right is a triangular prism. Find values of x and y so that the volume of the prism is between 80 ft³ and 100 ft³. Use your values for x and y and find the volume of the prism.

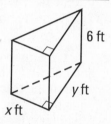

5. A spherical water storage tank has a 10-meter radius. If you double the radius, would twice as much water *fill* the tank? Would twice as much paint be enough to cover it? Explain your reasoning.

6. Give as much information as you can about the size of the can of corn and the can label shown at the right.

165

CHAPTER 12 TEST, Form D

Your school is planning to build a new running track. At the right is a rough sketch of the proposed track as it would appear when viewed from above. You have been asked to help plan the dimensions of the track and then prepare a report that summarizes important information for the people who will construct it. The only requirement is that one *lap*—a complete trip around the track—should be somewhere between 150 meters and 350 meters long.

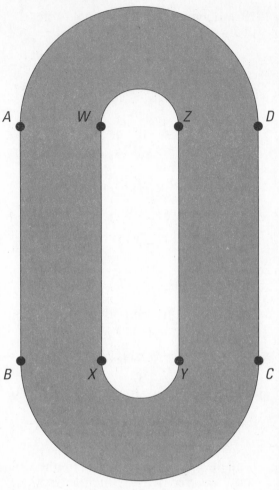

a. The shape of the track is formed by combining some simpler geometric shapes. What are the shapes?

b. What do you think would be appropriate dimensions for the track? Make a reasonable choice for each of these distances.

  i. A to B **ii.** A to D **iii.** W to X **iv.** W to Z

c. Use the dimensions that you chose in Part b and calculate the distance around the outer edge of the track (from A to B to C to D and back to A). Then calculate the distance around the inner edge (from W to X to Y to Z and back to W).

d. Did the dimensions you chose give you a track that is between 150 meters and 350 meters long? If they did not, adjust the dimensions until you have a track that meets this requirement.

e. Construction workers often use diagonal distances to check their work. If the track is constructed according to the dimensions you chose, what should each of the following distances be?

  i. A to C **ii.** B to D **iii.** W to Y **iv.** X to Z

f. What will be the total area of the track?

g. Just before the final running surface is laid, the track will be covered with a 10-cm layer of asphalt. What amount of asphalt will be needed?

Name _____

CHAPTER 12 TEST, Cumulative Form

1. *Multiple choice.* Real numbers include
   (a) rational numbers only.
   (b) irrational numbers only.
   (c) both rational and irrational numbers.

   1. _____

2. Write 6.28 as a simple fraction in lowest terms.

   2. _____

3. Simplify $-\sqrt{81}$.

   3. _____

4. Round $\sqrt{\pi}$ to the nearest hundreth.

   4. _____

5. A sector is $\frac{3}{8}$ of a circle. What is the measure of its central angle?

   5. _____

6. A square has area 8 ft². What is the exact length of a side of the square?

   6. _____

7. Write $.\overline{54}$ as a fraction in lowest terms.

   7. _____

8. Find the length of the diagonal of a square with side 3 in.

   8. _____

9. A 12-foot ladder needs to reach a gutter 10 feet off the ground. How far away from the side of the house should the foot of the ladder be placed?

   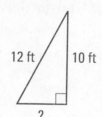

   9. _____

In 10-12, the spinner has a diameter of 5 in.

10. What is the circumference of the spinner?

    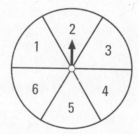

    10. _____

11. How much cardboard is needed to make the spinner?

    11. _____

12. What is the area of each sector if all central angles have the same measure?

    12. _____

Name _____

In 13 and 14, use this drawing of an unsharpened cylindrical pencil.

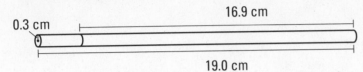

0.3 cm   16.9 cm

19.0 cm

13. Suppose the pencil measures 19.0 cm from end to end. The radius of the pencil is 0.3 cm. What is the volume of the entire pencil?

13. _____

14. The same pencil, without the eraser, measures only 16.9 cm in length. How much surface is covered by the yellow paint?

14. _____

In 15 and 16, use 5,276 km for the diameter of Ganymede, the largest of Jupiter's moons.

15. Determine the surface area of Ganymede, to the nearest million square kilometers.

15. _____

16. What is the volume of Ganymede, to the nearest million cubic kilometers?

16. _____

17. Explain the difference between a rational number and an irrational number.

_____

_____

_____

18. Simplify $\frac{3}{4} \div \frac{3}{8}$.

18. _____

19. Calculate a rate suggested by a 15-minute phone call costing $3.45.

19. _____

20. Simplify $-\frac{-20}{-4}$.

20. _____

21. Simplify $3m - 2n + m$.

21. _____

22. Suppose under a size change of magnitude k, the sides of the image are as long as sides of the preimage, but the image has been rotated 180° to get the image. What is k?

22. _____

23. How many lines of symmetry does a square have?

23. _____

24. *Multiple choice.* The expression $-x$

24. _____

    (a) is always negative.

    (b) is always positive.

    (c) can equal zero.

    (d) can equal any real number.

25. In the figure below, *TRAP* is similar to *ZOID*. Find *OI*.

25. _____

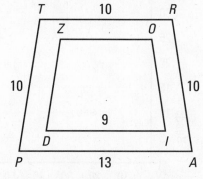

26. Just before Reggie Jackson's induction into the baseball Hall of Fame, he predicted that Ken Griffey, Jr., would hit 500 or more home runs in his career. Griffey hit 132 home runs during his first 5 seasons. At this rate, at least how many seasons must Griffey play to hit more than 500 home runs?

26. _____

Now check all your work carefully.

Name _____

QUIZ

1. Solve: $15 - 3y = 10y - 11$

1. _____

2. **a.** Graph the equations $y = 2x - 4$ and $y = -x + 5$ on the grid at the right.

   2. **a.**

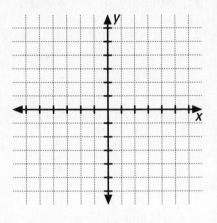

   b. Where do the lines intersect?

   b. _____

3. Consider the data in the table below, collected from tosses of a coin.

   3. **a.**

Total number of heads	Number of tosses
4	10
11	20
16	30
20	40
27	50

   a. Graph the data on the grid at the right.

   b. Do you think this coin is fair? Justify your answer by examining how these points fit with what you would expect.

   _____

   _____

   _____

   _____

   _____

CHAPTER 13 TEST, Form A

In 1 and 2, solve.

1. $14a + 3 = 11 - 2a$

1. _____

2. $5(2b - 1) = b + 4$

2. _____

In 3 and 4, graph the given equation on the grid at the right.

3., 4.

3. $y = 5x - 3$

4. $y = 3x$

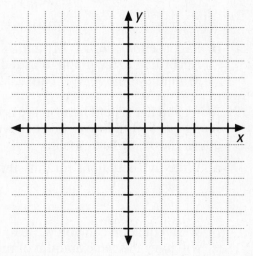

5. Explain how you can solve the equation $5x - 3 = 3x$ by using the graphs from Questions 3 and 4.

_____

_____

6. Evaluate $\lfloor 3.59 \rfloor$.

6. _____

7. If $\lceil c \rceil = -13$, give two possible values for c.

7. _____

8. *Multiple choice.* Consider this graph of how old Miranda says she is (y) compared to her actual age (x).

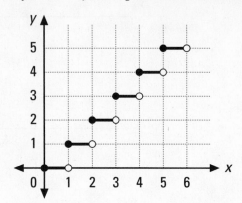

a. Which equation describes the graph?

(a) $y = x$ (c) $y = \lfloor x \rfloor$

(b) $y = \lceil x \rceil$ (d) $y = \lfloor x \rfloor + 1$

8. a. _____

b. Suppose *tomorrow* is Miranda's sixth birthday. According to the graph, if asked her age *today*, Miranda would reply, "I am ___?___ years old."

b. _____

9. Jeong and her sister Heewon are trying to save money. Jeong has $40 and saves $3 each week. Heewon has $32, but she saves $5 each week.

a. Write two equations for this situation.

9. a. _____

_____

b. What equation can you write to find when the sisters will have the same amount of money?

b. _____

c. Solve your equation from Part b.

c. _____

10. Oliver found a mistake in the following solution.

$$5x - 2 = 27x + 9$$

Step 1: $\quad$ $-5x + 5x - 2 = -5x + 27x + 9$

Step 2: $\quad\quad$ $0 - 2 = 22x + 9$

Step 3: $\quad\quad$ $-2 + 9 = 22x$

Step 4: $\quad\quad\quad$ $7 = 22x$

Step 5: $\quad\quad\quad$ $\frac{7}{22} = x$

a. Which step contains the mistake?

10. a. _____

b. Determine the correct solution.

b. _____

In 11-13, use this information: In a regular pentagon, the perimeter P and the length s of a side are related by the formula $P = 5s$.

11. Graph this formula for values of s from 0 to 6.

11.

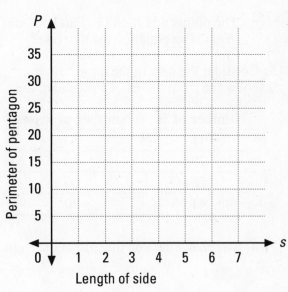

12. a. What is the perimeter of a regular pentagon with side length 3 cm?

12. a. _____

b. What point on the graph of $P = 5s$ is determined by the answer to Part a?

b. _____

13. Explain why quadrants II to IV are not needed for the graph of the formula in Question 11.

_____

_____

14. Consider the fraction $\frac{2}{3}$.

    a. Name four different fractions equal to it.

    b. For each fraction $\frac{a}{b}$, plot the ordered
       pair (b, a) on the axes at right.

14. a. _____

b.

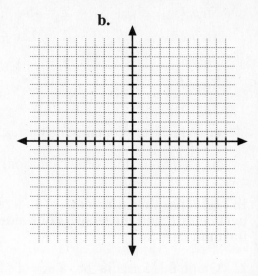

    c. The points you found in Part b should lie on a line.
       What is an equation for that line?

c. _____

15. Consider the data in the table below,
collected from tosses of a six-sided die.

Number of 5s	Number of tosses
11	20
23	40
28	60
41	80

    a. Graph the data on the grid at the right.

15. a.

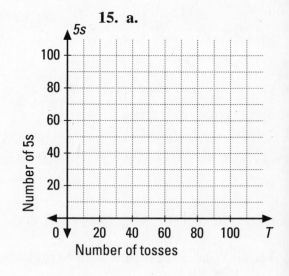

    b. Do you think this die is fair? Explain
       why or why not.

_____

_____

_____

Now check all your work carefully.

CHAPTER 13 TEST, Form B

In 1 and 2, solve.

1. $\frac{1}{3}r + 5 = -\frac{2}{5}r + 12$ **1.** _____

2. $7(2 - 5y) = 5y + 74$ **2.** _____

In 3 and 4, graph the given equation on the grid at the right.

3., 4.

3. $y = x - 6$

4. $y = -2x$

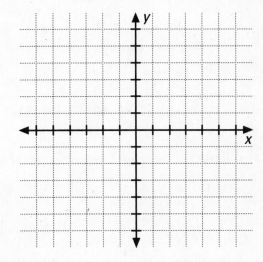

5. Explain how you can solve the equation $x - 6 = -2x$ by using the graphs from Questions 3 and 4.

_____

_____

6. Evaluate $\left\lceil \frac{2}{3} \right\rceil$.   **6.** _____

7. If $\lfloor r \rfloor = -6$, give two possible values for r.   **7.** _____

8. *Multiple choice.* Consider this graph of the number of burlap bags needed (y) to hold a certain weight of sand (x).

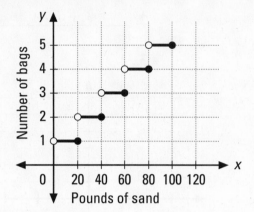

a. Which equation describes the graph?

(a) $y = \left\lceil \dfrac{x}{20} \right\rceil$ (c) $y = \dfrac{\lfloor x \rfloor}{20}$

(b) $y = \left\lfloor \dfrac{x}{20} \right\rfloor$ (d) $y = \lceil x \rceil - 20$

8. a. _____

b. Suppose you have 75 pounds of sand. How many burlap bags will you need?

b. _____

9. Car A and car B are traveling along the same road outside Houston. Car A is 100 miles from Houston and is moving *toward* the city at 50 miles per hour. Car B is 20 miles from Houston and is moving *away* from the city at 40 miles per hour.

a. What two equations describe this situation?

9. a. _____

b. What equation can you write to determine how much time it will take for the cars to pass each other?

_____

b. _____

c. Solve your equation from Part b.

c. _____

10. Olivia found a mistake in the following solution.

$$24x - 1 = -4x - 8$$

Step 1: $\quad 4x + 24x - 1 = 4x + -4x - 8$

Step 2: $\qquad 28x - 1 = 0 - 8$

Step 3: $\qquad\quad 28x = -8 - 1$

Step 4: $\qquad\quad 28x = 9$

Step 5: $\qquad\qquad x = \frac{-9}{28}$

    a. Which step contains the mistake?

    b. Determine the correct solution.

10. a. _____

    b. _____

In 11-13, use this information: In the isosceles right triangle below (both legs are of equal length), the area A and the length s of a leg are related by the formula $A = \frac{1}{2}s^2$.

11. Graph this formula for values of s from 0 to 7.

11.

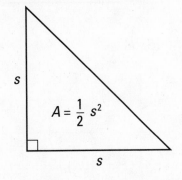

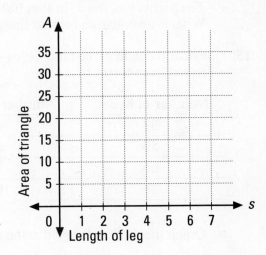

12. a. What is the area of the right triangle if both legs have length 4 cm?

    b. What point on the graph of $A = \frac{1}{2} s^2$ is determined by the answer to Part a?

12. a. _____

    b. _____

13. Explain why quadrants II to IV are not needed for the graph of the formula in Question 11.

_____

_____

14. Consider the fraction $\frac{-3}{2}$.

    a. Name four different fractions equal to it.

    14. a. _____

    b. For each fraction $\frac{a}{b}$, plot the ordered pair (b, a) on the grid at the right.

        b.

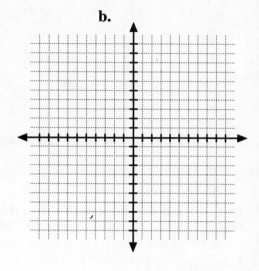

    c. The points you found in Part b should lie on a line. What is an equation for that line?

    c. _____

15. Consider the data in the table below, collected from tosses of a coin.

    15. a.

Number of heads	Number of tosses
33	40
50	60
66	80
78	100

    a. Graph the data on the grid at the right.

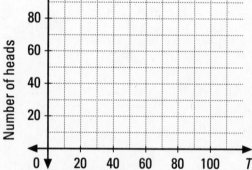

    b. Do you think this coin is fair? Explain why or why not.

_____

_____

_____

Now check all your work carefully.

CHAPTER 13 TEST, Form C

1. Arrange these equations in a more sensible order. Tell how you chose the order. What is the solution of each of the equations?

   a. $\quad 5 = -3 - 16x$

   b. $\quad 8 = -16x$

   c. $5 + 9x - 9x = -3 - 7x - 9x$

   d. $\quad 5 + 9x = -3 - 7x$

   e. $\quad 3 + 5 = 3 + -3 - 16x$

2. Graph each equation.

   a. $y = x$ $\qquad$ b. $y = \lfloor x \rfloor$

   c. $y = \lceil x \rceil$ $\qquad$ d. $y = x^2$

   Describe the shape of each graph.

3. Which of these points does *not* lie on the same line as all the others?

   (6, -4)   (9, -6)   (-9, 6)   (4, -6)   (12, -8)

   Tell how you know. Then give an equation for the line on which the other points lie.

4. a. Find a value of x such that $\lceil x \rceil$ does not equal x.

   b. Are there any values of x for which $\lceil x \rceil$ equals $\lfloor x \rfloor$?

   Explain your reasoning.

5. The graph at the right shows the costs of canoe rentals at two shops. Describe the cost at each shop in your own words. What information do you get from the point (3, 6)? How could you get the same information without the graph?

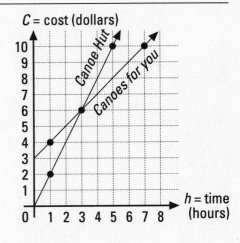

179

CHAPTER 13 TEST, Form D

Many people use a package delivery service to send items that weigh one pound or more. The amount that the service charges to deliver the package may depend upon the distance it must travel from the *point of origin.* To make it easier for a customer to determine this distance, the service may separate the fifty states into *zones* using guidelines like those at the right.

Zone Number	Approximate Distance from Point of Origin
1	less than 500 mi
2	500–1000 mi
3	1000–1500 mi
4	1500–2000 mi
5	more than 2000 mi

a. Suppose that you are establishing a small-package delivery service that will operate out of a city somewhere in the 48 "connected" states. Locate the city on the map below. This is your point of origin. Using the guidelines at the right, determine which states would be in each of your five zones. (*Hint:* Start by using a compass with its radius set to "500 miles.")

b. What do you think you would charge to send a one-pound package from your point of origin to each of your five zones?

c. What do you think you would charge for each additional pound that a package weighs? Make a table showing delivery charges for packages that weigh from one pound to ten pounds for each of the five zones. Then write an equation that represents the cost of delivery to each zone.

d. You have decided to create a brochure to advertise your new service. Make a graph of your rates that can be included in the brochure.

to Alaska 500 miles

SCALE
500 miles

to Hawaii 2500 miles

Alaska and Hawaii are not drawn to scale.

CHAPTER 13 TEST, Cumulative Form

Pythagorean Theorem	$a^2 + b^2 = c^2$
Volume of a cylindric solid	$V = hB$
Circumference of a circle	$C = \pi d$
Surface area of a sphere	$S = 4\pi r^2$
Area of a circle	$A = \pi r^2$
Volume of a sphere	$V = \frac{4}{3}\pi r^3$

In 1-3, solve

1. $13k + 7 = -k - 21$

1. _____

2. $5(\frac{1}{6}r + 1) = \frac{3}{2}r + 2 - \frac{4}{3}r$

2. _____

3. $\dfrac{x - 2}{5} = \dfrac{x}{4}$

3. _____

4. a. Graph the equations $y = -3x + 2$ and $y = 2x + 2$ on the grid at the right.

4. a.

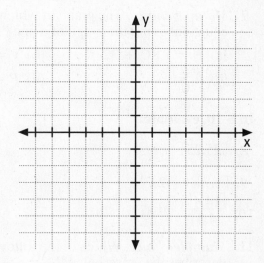

b. At what point do these lines intersect?

b. _____

5. Raphael is 1.4 m tall and is growing at a rate of 3 cm a year. Juana is 1.5 m tall and is growing at a rate of 1 cm a year.

a. Write two equations which describe this situation.

5. a. _____

_____

b. What equation can you solve to determine when they are the same height?

b. _____

c. Solve your equation from Part b.

c. _____

6. Consider the fraction $\frac{-3}{5}$.

　　a. Name three different fractions equal to it.

　　b. For each fraction $\frac{a}{b}$, plot the pair (b, a)
　　　　on the grid at the right.

6. a. _____

b.

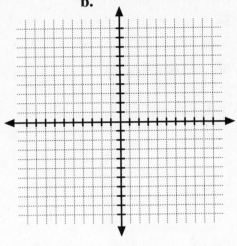

　　c. The points you found in Part b should lie on a line.
　　　　What is an equation for that line?

c. _____

7. *Multiple choice.* The graph of which of the following
　　equations is *not* the graph of a line?

7. _____

　　(a) $F = 1.8C + 32$　　　　(b) $y = -2x + 3$

　　(c) $A = s^2$　　　　　　　(d) $P = 5s$

In 8-10, evaluate.

8. $\lceil 25.25 \rceil$

8. _____

9. $\lceil 1.7 \rceil + \lfloor -2.7 \rfloor$

9. _____

10. $\dfrac{\lceil 14.4 \rceil}{\lceil 4.4 \rceil}$

10. _____

11. *Multiple choice.* Which of the following equations
　　describes the graph below?

11. _____

　　(a) $y = 2\lfloor x \rfloor$　　(b) $y = \lceil x \rceil + 2$

　　(c) $y = \lfloor x \rfloor$　　　(d) $y = \lfloor x \rfloor - 2$

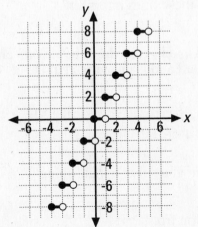

▶ **CHAPTER 13 TEST,** **Cumulative Form** *page 3*

12. *Multiple choice.* Which number is irrational?   **12.** _____

    (a) $\sqrt{81}$ (b) $-\sqrt{4}$

    (c) $\dfrac{\sqrt{25}}{5}$ (d) $\dfrac{\sqrt{3}}{1}$

In 13-14, find a simple fraction in lowest terms equal to the given number.

13. $1.0\overline{4}$ **13.** _____

14. $.2\overline{84}$ **14.** _____

In 15-16, find the missing length. Give an exact answer.

15.   **15.** _____

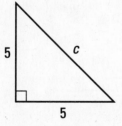

16.   **16.** _____

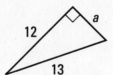

In 17 and 18, use the cylindric solid pictured below.

17. Find its total surface area   **17.** _____
to the nearest .01 square
centimeter.

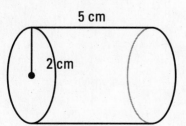

18. Find its volume to the   **18.** _____
nearest .01 cubic centimeter.

19. Between which two consecutive integers is $\sqrt{97}$?

19. _____

20. Simplify $1\frac{1}{5} \div \frac{1}{4}$.

20. _____

21. Use the Quotient-Remainder Theorem to write an equation relating the divisor, dividend, quotient, and remainder in this division problem.

$$\begin{array}{r} 6\ \text{R4} \\ 7\overline{)46} \end{array}$$

21. _____

22. Translate into an algebraic expression: six less than four times a number

22. _____

In 23-25, use the following information: You make a random choice from a bag of green, yellow, and red chips. The probability of choosing a green chip is $\frac{1}{5}$. The probability of choosing a yellow chip is $\frac{1}{4}$.

23. What is the probability of choosing a green chip or a yellow chip?

23. _____

24. What is the probability of choosing a red chip?

24. _____

25. If there are 40 chips in the bag, how many are green?

25. _____

Now check all your work carefully.

COMPREHENSIVE TEST, Chapters 1-13

In 1-25, *multiple choice.* **Give the letter of the correct answer.**

1. Eight thousandths is ___?___ .

   (a) .008   (b) .0008

   (c) 800.0   (d) 8000

1. _____

2. Which of the following is *not* equal to the other three?

   (a) $\frac{10}{3}$ (b) 3.3

   (c) $\frac{30}{9}$ (d) $3.\overline{3}$

2. _____

3. $10^{-4} =$ ___?___

   (a) -.4   (b) -10,000

   (c) .00001   (d) .0001

3. _____

4. According to the 1990 census, about 0.54% of the U.S. population 5 years or older speak Chinese at home. If, in 1990, the total U.S. population 5 years or older was about 230.5 million, approximately how many Americans spoke Chinese at home?

   (a) 12,447   (b) 124,470

   (c) 1,244,700   (d) 12,447,000

4. _____

5. To the nearest centimeter, how many centimeters are in a foot?

   (a) 30 cm   (b) 31 cm

   (c) 30.48 cm   (d) 30.5 cm

5. _____

6. It is impossible for a triangle to have

   (a) only one acute angle.   (b) 2 acute angles.

   (c) 3 acute angles.   (d) equal acute angles.

6. _____

7. Evaluate $-2x + y$ when $x = -3$ and $y = -4$.

   (a) -10   (b) 10

   (c) 2   (d) -2

7. _____

8. Which of the following has the same solutions as $b < 8$?

   (a) $b \leq 8$ (b) $8 < b$

   (c) $8 > b$ (d) $8 \geq b$

8. _____

Name _____

9. Which number line shows -4 + 6?

9. _____

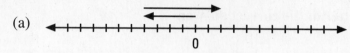

   (a)

   (b)

   (c)

   (d)

10. Which equation illustrates the Associative Property of Addition?

10. _____

   (a) (3 + 2) + 1 = (2 + 3) + 1   (b) 3 + 2 = 2 + 3
   (c) (3 + 2) + 1 = 3 + (2 + 1)   (d) 3 (2 + 1) = 3 • 2 + 3 • 1

11. Which is a solution to $(m + 3)(m - 2) = m^2$?

11. _____

   (a) 3   (b) 4
   (c) 5   (d) 6

12. Which equals -3 − -6?

12. _____

   (a) -6 − -3   (b) 3 + 6
   (c) -3 + 6   (d) -3 + -6

13. Which of the following is always a rhombus?

13. _____

   (a) parallelogram   (b) rectangle
   (c) trapezoid   (d) square

14. According to the graph below, which of the following statements is *false*?

14. _____

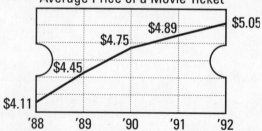

Average Price of a Movie Ticket

$5.05
$4.89
$4.75
$4.45
$4.11
'88   '89   '90   '91   '92

   (a) The average cost of a movie ticket went up every year from 1988 to 1992.

   (b) The biggest increase was from 1988 to 1989.

   (c) To know which movie was seen in theaters by the most people in 1988 to 1992, look for the movie that took in the most money at the box office.

15. Which point is *not* on the line $y = 3x + 2$?   15. _____

    (a) (-2, -4)   (b) (1, 3)

    (c) (0, 2)   (d) (2, 8)

16. What is the area of a rectangle 1 ft long and 6 in. wide?   16. _____

    (a) 6 in.^{2} (b) 6 ft^2

    (c) $\frac{1}{2}$ ft^2 (d) 36 in.^{2}

17. In a size change of $-\frac{1}{2}$, which of the following is *false?*   17. _____

    (a) The image is smaller than the preimage.

    (b) The preimage is rotated 180°.

    (c) The image is similar to the preimage.

    (d) The angle measures in the image are half the angle measures in
        the preimage.

18. A right triangle has sides 6, 8, and 10. Its area is   18. _____

    (a) 48.   (b) 24.

    (c) 30.   (d) 40.

19. The amount of air in a room would be measured in   19. _____

    (a) feet.   (b) square feet.

    (c) cubic feet.   (d) meters.

20. Which of the following is the integer division answer to $8 \div 3$?   20. _____

    (a) $\frac{8}{3}$ (b) $2\frac{2}{3}$

    (c) $2.\overline{6}$ (d) 2 with a remainder of 2

21. If the triangles below are similar with corresponding pairs of sides   21. _____
parallel, $DO =$ ___?___

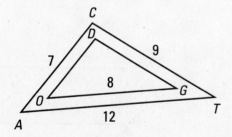

    (a) $4\frac{2}{3}$ (b) 10.5

    (c) $1\frac{1}{6}$ (d) $\frac{6}{7}$

► **COMPREHENSIVE TEST,** Chapters 1-13 *page 4*

22. Which of the following is an irrational number?   22. _____
    (a) $\sqrt{2}$ (b) $\sqrt{4}$
    (c) $\frac{7}{2}$ (d) $.\overline{3}$

23. Which of the following could *not* be the sides of a right triangle?   23. _____
    (a) 3, 4, 5   (b) 4, 5, 6
    (c) 6, 8, 10   (d) 5, 12, 13

24. The graph of which of the following equations is a line?   24. _____
    (a) $y = \lfloor x \rfloor$ (b) $y = \lceil x \rceil$
    (c) $y = x$ (d) $y = x^2$

25. Which is a solution to $\lfloor m \rfloor = 6$?   25. _____
    (a) 5.8   (b) $6\frac{3}{4}$
    (c) 7   (d) 7.01

In 26 and 27, solve.

26. $\frac{2}{3}x = 6$ 26. _____

27. $4(3 - 2t) = 4t$ 27. _____

28. Evaluate: $\dfrac{4(3 + 2)^2}{8 - -12}$ 28. _____

29. a. Write a key sequence to enter   29. a. _____
       $380{,}000{,}000 \div .00000002$ on
       your calculator.

    b. Write the answer as a decimal.   b. _____

30. How long is the diagonal of a square   30. _____
    5 ft on a side? Give an exact answer.

31. Find each measure.

   a. m∠1

   b. m∠2

   c. m∠3

   d. m∠4

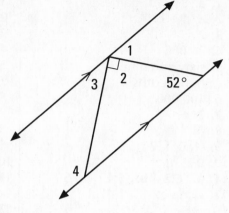

31. a. _____

   b. _____

   c. _____

   d. _____

32. Find the surface area of this box.

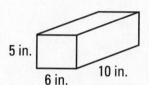

5 in.

6 in.   10 in.

32. _____

33. An airplane is flying at 10,000 ft. To the nearest tenth of a mile, how high is the plane?

33. _____

34. 45% of Mr. Malcom's math students got an A or a B. If 54 students earned an A or a B, how many students does Mr. Malcom teach?

34. _____

35. Graph $y = 3x - 1$.

35.

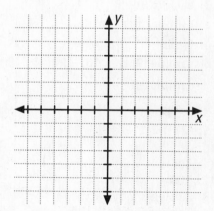

Now check all your work carefully.

Answers and Evaluation Guides*

Quiz — Lessons 1–1 Through 1–4

1. a. 605,694 b. live births
2. 9,999,999
3. 4.03; 4.3; 4.34
4. sample: 21.35
5. a. 10 b. 11
6. a. .5 b. D
7. a. 0.75 b. 0.74 c. 0.75
8. (d)
9. 13.2 seconds
10. Answers may vary. Sample: A calculator that displays only 8 digits shows that $65,329 \div 39 = 1675.1025$. A calculator with a larger display shows 1675.102564. The first truncates to the preceding ten-thousandth place.

Quiz — Lessons 1–5 Through 1–8

1. 2.625
2. $0.\overline{63}$
3. a. 136 b. 8 c. 17
4. sample: 152
5. $49 \div 63 =$
6. sample: $9 \pm + 16 - 20 =$
7. sample: -8
8. $\frac{3}{5}, \frac{33}{50}, \frac{2}{3}$
9. $-2\frac{1}{5}, -2\frac{3}{16}, -2\frac{2}{11}$
10. -4
11. 50
12. 100
13. Answers may vary. The integers are the counting numbers, their opposites, and zero.

Chapter 1 Test, Form A

1. a. 84 b. games
2. a. 1 b. 4
3. 2
4. 31,006
5. sixty and nine hundredths
6. 100,000
7. 24¢
8. (d)
9. -1, 0, 1, 2
10. 0.2
11. a. -6.2 b. -5.4 c. -5
12. sample: -1
13. $.31 < 3.\overline{1} < 3.12$
14. $-15 < -5$
15. 247.8
16. 248
17. 240
18. 16
19. 3
20. sample: $\frac{3}{4}$
21. sample: 13.45
22. 2.0625
23. $12.\overline{45}$
24. $\frac{169}{6}$, or $28\frac{1}{6}$
25. 3
26. $2\frac{6}{7}$
27. -3.75

-4 -3 -2 -1 0 1 2 3 4

28. $\frac{8}{17}$; sample: $\frac{16}{34}$
29. $\frac{59}{99}$
30. $\frac{1}{3}$
31. $7\frac{2}{3}$
32. 999,990
33. 950
34. 1050
35. 9
36. (d)
37. 1, 3, 17, 51
38. 32
39. 17 feet below sea level
40. Answers may vary. sample: Round off to $13. Multiply $13 \times 3 = 39$. Estimate the cost to be about $39.

Chapter 1 Test, Form B

1. a. 7,748 b. windows
2. a. 8 b. 1
3. 5
4. 40,005
5. fifty-two and seven hundredths
6. 9,999
7. $9.67
8. (c)
9. -2, -1, 0, 1, 2, 3
10. 0.2
11. a. 7.6 b. 8.6 c. 9.2
12. sample: -1.5
13. $.41 > -4.1 > -41$
14. $-5 > -16$
15. 105.7
16. 106
17. 100
18. 10
19. 4
20. sample: $\frac{9}{40}$
21. sample: 6.25
22. .1875
23. $16.\overline{6}$
24. $\frac{5}{6}$
25. 2
26. $3\frac{1}{9}$
27. -2.5

-5 -4 -3 -2 -1 0 1 2 3 4

28. $\frac{7}{12}$; sample: $\frac{14}{24}$
29. $\frac{19}{25}$
30. $\frac{1}{3}$
31. $8\frac{5}{7}$
32. 999,996
33. 850
34. 950
35. 11
36. (a)
37. 1, 2, 3, 4, 6, 8, 12, 16, 24, 48
38. 8
39. $69.85
40. Answers may vary. sample: round off to $14. Multiply $14 \times 4 = 56$. Estimate the cost to be about $56.

*Evaluation Guides for Chapter Tests, Forms C and D, are on pages 214–239.

Quiz — Lessons 2–1 Through 2–3

1. 326,000
2. 700,000
3. a. The exponent
   b. The base
4. 5^6
5. (b)
6. a. 1,320,000,000,000
   b. 1.32×10^{12}
7. 307,200,000
8. sample: 3.485 Exp 10
9. 34,850,000,000,000 kg
10. Answers may vary. sample: Scientific notation allows us to write very large or very small numbers in short form.

Quiz — Lessons 2–4 Through 2–6

1. 0.0347
2. 0.0006
3. 60
4. 41.25
5. .25
6. 25%
7. $\frac{17}{200}$
8. 8.5%
9. $\frac{18}{25}$
10. .72
11. $\frac{2}{3}$
12. $66\frac{2}{3}\%$
13. $.41\overline{6}$
14. $41\frac{2}{3}\%$
15. $\frac{1}{200}$
16. .005
17. $104.29
18. 674 women

Chapter 2 Test, Form A

1. 48,000
2. .026
3. 3,950,000
4. 625
5. 76,000,000
6. .000026
7. .000029
8. 428,000
9. .08
10. 75; 50
11. six trillion
12. one hundred-thousandth
13. one
14. 4.62×10^6
15. 3×10^9
16. 1×10^{-5}
17. 7.5×10^{-9}
18. three to the fifth power
19. The base is not 10.
20. 4^6
21. 0
22. $\frac{1}{5}$
23. -$4.3 billion
24. sample: 8.5 Exp 9
25. >
26. a. paper   b. glass
27. all municipal solid wastes
28. $283.50
29. a. D b. $\overline{AB}$
30. Answers may vary. sample: Scientific notation makes it possible to write long numbers in shorter form.
31. .75
32. 75%
33. $\frac{9}{20}$
34. .45
35. $\frac{1}{3}$
36. $33\frac{1}{3}\%$
37. $2\frac{1}{2}$
38. 2.5
39. $\frac{1}{200}$
40. .5%

Chapter 2 Test, Form B

1. 575,000
2. .42
3. 6,290,000,000
4. 216
5. 920,000,000
6. .000026
7. .000029
8. .000629
9. .08
10. 20; 50
11. eight million
12. one thousandth
13. ten
14. 3.296×10^9
15. 4×10^7
16. 1×10^{-3}
17. 5×10^{-9}
18. four to the third power
19. 321 is not between 1 and 10.
20. 5^6
21. 1
22. $\frac{1}{2}$
23. $2.42 billion
24. sample: 4.7 Exp 12
25. >
26. a. 30 − 39 years
    b. under 12 years
27. total deaths by AIDS from 1982–91
28. $16.17
29. center H; radius $\overline{GH}$, $\overline{EH}$, or $\overline{FH}$
30. Answers may vary. sample: The numbers can be written in shorter form, and they can be entered into a calculator.
31. .6
32. 60%
33. $\frac{1}{4}$
34. .25
35. $\frac{2}{3}$
36. $66\frac{2}{3}\%$
37. $3\frac{1}{10}$
38. 3.1
39. $\frac{1}{500}$
40. .2%

Chapter 2 Test, Cumulative Form

1. 3790
2. 300,000,000
3. .0085
4. .000000007
5. .000492
6. .625
7. 80,800,000
8. $7.\overline{6}$
9. .0008
10. .032
11. 100,000,000
12. 1
13. 512
14. .2666
15. .00001
16. ⁻3
17. the base
18. the exponent
19. 4^6
20. sample: 6$\boxed{y^x}$4
21. $\frac{79}{100}$
22. 0.79
23. $.58\overline{3}$
24. $58.\overline{3}\%$
25. $\frac{163}{100}$
26. 163%
27. 32
28. 7.5
29. a. I b. W c. D d. M
    e. N
30. 3.5×10^{-10}
31. $52,500
32. sample: 197 $\boxed{Exp}$ 6
33. 57 million square miles
34. Taco Bell, Burger King, and other; or McDonald's, Wendy's, and Pizza Hut
35. 78
36. Answers may vary. samples: You can understand the number when different sources use different forms. You can select a form that is best for the situation.

Quiz — Lessons 3–1 Through 3–3

1. 5280
2. 2.54
3. 8
4. 4
5. 16
6. (a)
7. (c)
8. (c)
9. (d)
10. a. $3\frac{1}{2}$ inches
    b. $3\frac{5}{8}$ inches   c. 9 cm
    d. 93 mm
11. See below.
12. Answers may vary.

Quiz — Lessons 3–4 Through 3–7

1. 1000
2. .001
3. 100
4. 2.2
5. .62
6. 1.06
7. 4500 g
8. more
9. ≈ .93 mi; 24.8 mi; 6.2 mi
10. sample:

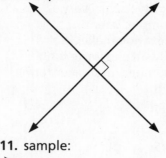

11. sample:

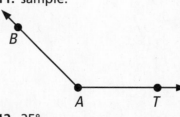

12. 25°
13. 115°

Chapter 3 Test, Form A

1. (c)
2. (b)
3. (a)
4. (d)
5. (b)
6. milliliters
7. kilograms
8. square feet
9. 1000
10. 8600
11. 8
12. 2000
13. $1\frac{1}{4}$ in.
14. 26 mm
15. 135°
16. $\angle M$
17. $\angle A, \angle E$
18. No
19.

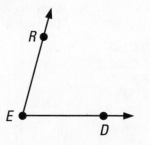

20.

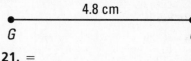

4.8 cm

G   O

21. =
22. ≈
23. >
24. <
25. ≈ 3330 lb
26. ≈ 2490 mi
27. 1,000,000 mm
28. 8 cups
29. a. 50%   b. 180°
    c. 20%   d. 72°
    e. 30%   f. 108°
30.

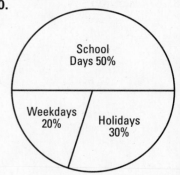

11. _____ 12.5 cm

Chapter 3 Test, Form B

1. (a)
2. (b)
3. (b)
4. (a)
5. (b)
6. liters
7. grams
8. square inches
9. 5000
10. 9400
11. 16
12. 4
13. $1\frac{1}{4}$ in.
14. 39 mm
15. 90°
16. none
17. ∠E, ∠R, ∠A
18. 8000 cm³
19.

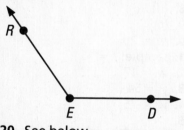

20. See below.
21. >
22. >
23. ≈
24. >
25. ≈ 2750 lb
26. ≈ 4154 mi
27. 100,000 cm
28. 64 fl oz
29. a. 60%   b. 216°
    c. 30%   d. 108°
    e. 10%   f. 36°
30.

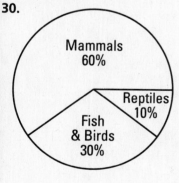

Chapter 3 Test, Cumulative Form

1. 5280
2. 2.54
3. 2000
4. 1000
5. 2.2
6. 1000
7. milligram
8. cup, pint or fluid ounce
9. centimeter
10. 2.342 L
11. 12 pints
12. ≈ 1029.2 mi
13. 9 ft 6 in.
14. a.

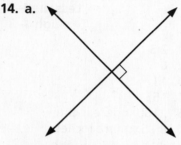

   b. right angle
15. a.

   b. 2.25 cm²
16. a. 35 mm   b. $1\frac{3}{8}$ in.
17. a. 25°   b. ∠N
18. =
19. <
20. <
21. ≈
22. 512 in³
23. 3,000,000,000
24. .0007
25. $.8\overline{3}$
26. 7.25
27. .0000001
28. 5.625
29. 420,000
30. .005
31. a. 56.76%   b. about 44 million people
32. a. $\frac{6}{9}$ b. $\frac{13}{4}$ c. $\frac{20}{4}$
    d. $\frac{1}{3}$ e. $\frac{2}{5}$

33. a. 42,000,000
    b. 41,000,000
    c. 41,000,000
    d. 4.1×10^7
    e. 41 million

20.   5.2 cm
    R ●————————————● V

ANSWERS

Comprehensive Test, Chapters 1–3

1. (c)
2. (c)
3. (d)
4. (a)
5. (b)
6. (c)
7. (c)
8. (b)
9. (c)
10. (d)
11. (c)
12. (b)
13. (c)
14. (a)
15. (c)
16. (b)
17. (b)
18. (b)
19. (c)
20. (d)
21. (a)
22. (b)
23. (c)
24. (d)
25. (d)
26. a. 13,135,307,000
    b. 13,135,000,000
    c. 13,136,000,000
    d. 13,000,000,000
27. a. 7 ÷ 12 =
    b. sample: 0.5833333333
28. See below.
29. a. 2.193×10^{11}
    b. 2×10^{-9}
30. a. 50%   b. 25%
    c. 12.5%
31. $7.81
32. 8 pt
33. 91.44 cm
34. a. 32 mm   b. $1\frac{3}{8}$ in.
    c. 63°
35. 6.15×10^{13}
36. Answers may vary.

Quiz   Lessons 4–1 Through 4–4

1. 27
2. 17
3. sample: $x - 6$
4. sample. $6 < x$
5. sample: $6 - n$
6. $c + 7 - y$
7. sample: $x^4 = x \cdot x \cdot x \cdot x$
8. sample: $5 + 5 + 7 + 7 = 2(5) + 2(7)$
9. $2.02
10. a. $36.50   b. $2.50

Quiz   Lessons 4–5 Through 4–8

1. 2.3
2. 6
3. 11
4. 155
5. 2160 square inches
6. 8.25 square inches
7. 30.4
8. 86.25
9. $\frac{11}{30}$

Chapter 4 Test, Form A

1. (b)
2. variable
3. sample: x folders have $x \cdot 2$ pockets
4. sample: $a \times b = b \times a$
5. samples: $5 + 0 = 5$, $27 + 0 = 27$
6. $\frac{7n}{7 + n}$
7. $2n + 10$
8. $-12 < n$
9. $9 - n$
10. $n - 9$
11. (a)
12. 78
13. 37
14. 13
15. 575
16. 38
17. 23.5
18. (d)
19. (c)
20. $m = 20$
21. sample: $t = -6$
22. $w = 17$
23. $y = 54$
24. $w > -75$
25.

26. 144 ft
27. .330
28. a. $\frac{5}{12}$ b. $\frac{7}{12}$
29. Answers may vary. sample: No; you would expect 3 to be shown about $\frac{1}{6}$ of the time, which is about 17 times.

28.

Chapter 4 Test, Form B

1. (d)
2. sample: A pattern is a general idea for which there are many examples. An example of a pattern is an instance.
3. sample: x watches have $x \cdot 3$ hands
4. sample: $-(a - b) = b - a$
5. samples: $6 + 6 = 2(6)$; $8 + 8 = 2(8)$
6. $\frac{12}{3n}$
7. $\frac{1}{2}n - 7$
8. $-2 > n$
9. $15 - n$
10. $n - 15$
11. (c)
12. 39
13. 140
14. 23
15. 153
16. 36.5
17. 18.5
18. (c)
19. (d)
20. sample: $t < -1$
21. $m = 38$
22. $w = 24$
23. $y = 42$
24. $z < -40$
25.

    -3 -2 -1 0 1 2 3 t

26. ≈ 113.1 sq ft
27. 70.8%
28. $\frac{17}{35}$
29. Answers may vary. sample: A probability of 1 means that an event is certain to happen. Since $P = \frac{E}{N}$, where N is the number of outcomes possible for the situation and E is the number of outcomes for the event E, and since $E \leq N$, then P can never be greater than 1.

Chapter 4 Test, Cumulative Form

1. 2^2
2. sample: $3 \times 5 + 5 = 4 \times 5$
3. sample: $\frac{x}{10}$
4. $(x + y) \div (x - y)$
5. $p = .25b$
6. $\frac{6}{11}$
7. 60%, or .6
8. $r = 12$
9. (c)
10. sample: $s = -2$
11.

    m

    0

12. See right.
13. 22.75
14. 4
15. 2
16. sample: $8a + 8b = 8(a + b)$
17. $10t + 15f + 20w$
18. .343
19. $-3 > q \geq -6$
20. sample: Relative frequency is calculated from the observed number of outcomes in an experiment; probability is calculated from the theoretical number of outcomes.
21. 36
22. .5
23. mg
24. ray HI
25. $\frac{1}{4}$ square inch
26. 5,500,000,000
27. 3×10^{-10}
28. $\frac{3}{5}$
29. 56,000
30. $\frac{23}{25}$
31. 3274
32. 8 feet 4 inches

33.

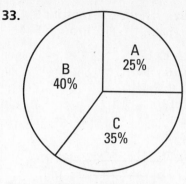

34. samples: 3.6 [Exp] 8 [=]
    3.6 [×] 10 [y^x] 8 [=]
35. $-2, -\frac{3}{5}, 6.3 \times 10^{-3}, 45\%$
36. a. $2\frac{7}{10}$ b. $\frac{27}{10}$ c. 270%
    d. 3

Quiz   **Lessons 5–1 Through 5–4**

1. -30.1
2. -5
3. -1.5
4. 17
5. 1
6. -3
7. 9
8.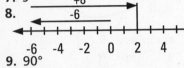

$$-6 \quad -4 \quad -2 \quad 0 \quad 2 \quad 4$$

9. 90°
10. -144°
11. a. 0   b. Answers may vary. sample: Adding 0 to a number keeps the identity of that number.
12. opposite
13. a. $15 + -7.25 + 9.5 + -6.75$ b. $10.50
14. a. Additive Identity Property of Zero
   b. Property of Opposites

Quiz   **Lessons 5–5 Through 5–8**

1. a. iv   b. ii   c. i   d. iii
2. $-\frac{1}{3}$
3. $-\frac{1}{6}$
4. $a = 7.4$
5. $c = 4\frac{5}{8}$
6. $p = \frac{2}{7} + \frac{1}{7} = \frac{3}{7}; \frac{3}{7}$
7. $93 + 82 + 91 + x = 360$; 94

Chapter 5 Test, Form A

1. -4.9   2. 4
3. 2   4. -16.5
5. 1.5   6. -3.5
7. $\frac{-1}{a}$ 8. $\frac{13}{12}$
9. (b)
10. sample: $10 + 0 = 10$
11. sample: B and C
12. $\frac{8}{13}$
13. Answers may vary. sample: The events are not mutually exclusive, so the probability is not found by adding their probabilities.
14. negative
15. $-19 = s$
16. $r = 4\frac{1}{2}$
17. $12.8 = d$
18. $f = 1\frac{1}{6}$
19. 225°
20. -315°
21. sample: $AS + AK = SK$
22. 2.5 cm
23. a. See below.   b. 5
24. $(60 + d)$ meters
25. $B + G + C + 1 = 31$
26. a. $-26 + p = 32$
   b. $p = 58$ pages
27. a. $7 + 7 + 3.2 + 3.2 + 4.5 + 4.5 + S = 38$
   b. $S = 8.6$ in.
28. sample: JOKES
29. 5
30. 113 mm
31. Answers will vary. sample: On a number line, draw an arrow from 0 to the negative number. Draw another arrow from the negative to the right as many units as the positive number.

Chapter 5 Test, Form B

1. -2.4   2. 13
3. 16   4. -17.5
5. 6.5   6. 8.1
7. $\frac{-6}{a}$ 8. $\frac{19}{15}$
9. (b)
10. (c)
11. A and C
12. $\frac{5}{8}$
13. Answers may vary. Sample: These events are not mutually exclusive, so the probability is not found by adding their probabilities.
14. positive
15. $17.6 = y$
16. $-22 = t$
17. $r = 11\frac{1}{2}$
18. $m = \frac{19}{8} = 2\frac{3}{8}$
19. 30°
20. -150°
21. sample: $PR + RQ = PQ$
22. 9.8 cm
23. a. See below.   b. -2
24. $(t + 5)$ meters
25. sample: $1 + P + Q = 47$
26. a. sample: $-7 + p = 3$
   b. $p = 10$ points
27. a. $2.5 + 2.5 + 9 + 7.5 + S = 28$ b. $S = 6.5$ cm
28. sample: TUESDAY
29. sample: $\overline{TD}$
30. 154 mm
31. Answers may vary sample: On a number line, draw an arrow from 0 to one number. Then draw an arrow from that number to the left as many units as the other number requires.

23. a.

$$+8$$
$$-3$$
$$-10 \qquad -5 \qquad 0 \qquad 5 \qquad 10$$

23. a.

$$-8$$
$$6$$
$$-10 \qquad -5 \qquad 0 \qquad 5 \qquad 10$$

Chapter 5 Test, Cumulative Form

1. 35.5 g or 35,500 mg
2. $n + -n = 0$
3. 10
4. sample: $\boxed{+/-}$ 3.25 $\boxed{+}$ 4.08 $\boxed{=}$
5. 1080°
6. $\frac{17}{5}$
7. $\frac{1}{2}$
8. sample: $2 + (4 + 5) = (2 + 4) + 5$
9. (c)
10. 12 cm
11. 1.3
12. p
13. $\frac{15}{n}$
14. $\frac{3}{20}$
15. $y = 6$
16. $p = 7\frac{1}{6}$
17. a. See below.   b. -2
18.

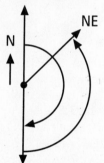

19. No. Sample: $1 \div 2 \neq 2 \div 1$
20. 71
21. 2.75
22. $-3.5 \leq x \leq 3$
23. sample: $(2x)^2 = 4x^2$
24. $n + 5$
25. $(k - 12)$ kg
26. $93\frac{1}{2}$ in.²
27. 5,600,000
28. 15.625
29. 2.5
30. $-3.1\overline{6}$
31. .0000072
32. sample:

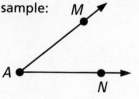

33. sample:

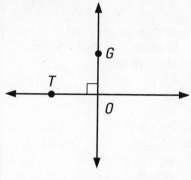

34.

I |——— 3.5 cm ———| M

1. Answers may vary. sample: A problem is a question that you do not know how to answer.
2. Answers may vary.
3. 8
4. Saturday
5. 167
6. 1, 2, 3, 4, 6, 8, 12, 24
7. $55\frac{1}{4}$ square inches

1. 24
2.

Number of Pieces	Measure of Central Angle
2	180°
3	120°
4	90°
5	72°
n	$\frac{360°}{n}$

3. $56.50; $(25 + 60n)$
4.

	A	B
1	-3	-35
2	-2	-12
3	-1	3
4	0	10
5	1	9
6	2	0
7	3	-17

5. $= 10 + 3\text{*}A1 - 4\text{*}A1\text{*}A1$
6. copy

ANSWERS

17. a.

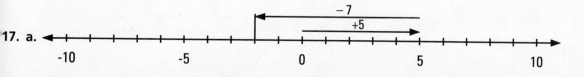

197

Chapter 6 Test, Form A

1. Answer may vary. sample: dictionary, geometry book
2. 53, 59
3. 9
4. (c)
5. 2.6 km
6. 5
7. $m = 2$, $n = 3$; or $m = 4$, $n = 2$
8. (b)
9. 1 and 32
10. (b)
11. 2; right
12.

	A	B
1	miles	Cost
2	10	21.05
3	20	22.15
4	30	23.25
5	n	.11*n+19.95

13. = A2+10
14. = 19.95+.11*A5
15. 8
16. a. sample: $x = 0$, $y = 1$
    b. sample: $x = 2$, $y = 3$
17. Sum = n^2

Chapter 6 Test, Form B

1. Answers may vary. sample: a dictionary, an algebra book
2. 61, 67
3. 14
4. (d)
5. 2.5 km
6. 5
7. $m = 2$, $n = 4$; or $m = 4$, $n = 2$
8. (b)
9. 4 and 8
10. (c)
11. 3, left
12.

	A	B
1	miles	Cost
2	10	30.85
3	20	31.75
4	30	32.65
5	n	29.95+.09*n

13. = A2+10
14. = 29.95+.09*A5
15. 27
16. a. sample: $x = 0$, $y = 0$
    b. sample: $x = 1$, $y = 0$
17. Sum = $n(n + 1)$

Chapter 6 Test, Cumulative Form

1. 51, 52, 54, 55, 56, 57, 58
2. 4, right
3. (d)
4. Answers may vary. sample: a dictionary, a geometry book
5. No; sample: $5(2 + 3) \neq 5 \cdot 2 + 3$
6. 10
7. 68 feet
8.

	A	B	C
1	10:45	10:50	7.46
2	10:50	10:55	=C1+5.60
3	10:55	11:00	=C2+5.60
4	11:00	11:05	=C3+4.25
5	11:05	11:10	=C4+4.25
6	11:10	11:15	=C5+4.25
7	11:15	11:20	=C6+4.25
8	11:20	11:25	=C7+4.25
9	11:25	11:30	=C8+4.25

9. $\frac{5}{9}$
10. $-y$
11. 8
12. (d)
13. .0001
14. $x = 5\frac{1}{2}$
15. 3475.67
16. a. .035   b. 3.5%
17. sample:

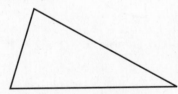

18. about 275 students
19. Answers will vary. sample: trial and error
20. Answers will vary. sample: Trial and error can be used when a question has only a few possible answers. Keep trying until an answer is found.

Comprehensive Test, Chapters 1–6

1. (c)
2. (b)
3. (c)
4. (c)
5. (d)
6. (a)
7. (d)
8. (b)
9. (a)
10. (d)
11. (b)
12. (d)
13. (a)
14. (c)
15. (b)
16. (a)
17. (d)
18. (a)
19. (c)
20. (c)
21. (b)
22. (c)
23. (b)
24. (b)
25. (c)
26. $23,378.24
27. about 31 miles
28. a. 25 mm b. 130°
29. 288 in.² or 2 ft²
30. a. $n - 10$ b. $10 - n$
    c. $10 < n$
31. $k = 2$
32. Jordan
33. Answers may vary. sample: formulas are recalculated when numbers are changed, saving time and avoiding errors.

Quiz Lessons 7–1 Through 7–4

1. -30
2. 14.5
3. $-2\frac{3}{4}$
4. $1\frac{4}{15}$
5. $b = 108$
6. $N = -23.45$
7. $K = 10$
8. $y = \frac{55}{24}$
9. a. $d = 26,200 - (-1,100)$
   b. 27,300 feet
10. a. $m = 7,410,000 - 960,000$
    b. $6,450,000
11. 80.01 cm²
12. No. Answers may vary. sample: for example, $7 - 9 = -2$ and $9 - 7 = 2$, so $7 - 9 \neq 9 - 7$.

Quiz Lessons 7–5 Through 7–8

1. 317
2. $\frac{5}{18}$
3. 110°
4. 70°
5. 90°
6. 148°
7. sample: $\angle 1$ and $\angle 3$
8. sample: $\angle 1$ and $\angle 2$
9. sample: $\angle 1$ and $\angle 8$
10. sample: $\angle 1$ and $\angle 6$

Chapter 7 Test, Form A

1. -4
2. -10.5
3. $\frac{5}{4}$
4. 4.9
5. $-3\frac{1}{3}$
6. $P = 4$
7. $Q = -31$
8. $R = -12$
9. a. $x - 1600 = 1612$
   b. $x = 3212$
   c. Angel Falls is 3212 feet high
10. a. $x = -13 - -40$
    b. $x = 27$
    c. The temperature changed 27°.
11. samples: $a = x + b$; $a + -x = b$; $x = a - b$
12. a. 40° b. 50° c. 40°
13. 72°
14. a. 4 b. 20° c. 110°
15. 76.25 cm²
16. 0
17. Science   Math

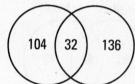

18. $\frac{8}{13}$
19. sample:

20. True
21. False
22. True
23. C
24. Answers may vary. sample: the sum of the 3 angles of a triangle is 180°; if 2 of the angles were obtuse, the sum would be greater than 180°.
25. a. See below. b. -11

25. a.

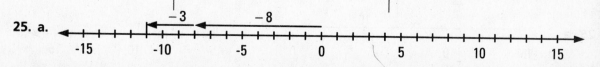

Chapter 7 Test, Form B

1. -6
2. -6.3
3. $\frac{7}{8}$
4. 4.9
5. $-\frac{13}{14}$
6. $P = -1$
7. $Q = -21$
8. $R = -20$
9. a. $x = 1454 - 245$
   b. $x = 1209$
   c. The Bank of China building is 1209 feet high.
10. a. $x = -13 - (-4)$
    b. $x = -9$
    c. The temperature went down 9°.
11. samples: $x = a - b$; $b = a - x$; $x - a = -b$
12. a. 25° b. 65° c. 25°
13. 17°
14. a. 4 b. 50° c. 140°
15. 252.96 cm²
16. -3
17.   Science   Math
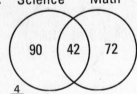
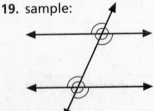
18. $\frac{4}{13}$
19. sample:

20. True
21. False
22. False
23. AD
24. Answers may vary. sample: the sum of the 3 angles would be more than 180°.
25. a. See below. b. -15

Chapter 7 Test, Cumulative Form

1. a. Answers may vary. sample: on a number line, slide 3 to the right, then 11 to the left.
   b. -8
2. a. Answers may vary. sample: use Opposite of Opposites Property to get $5 + 8$. Then add.
   b. 13
3. 11
4. $f = 1.9$
5. $y = 18$
6. $y = m + b$
7. 100°
8. regular decagon
9. False
10. 132°
11. 48°
12. 132°
13. 32.75 m²
14. sample: $853 - 642 = t$
15. 211
16. 46 students
17. $2.84
18. sample: Let $x = 4$, $y = 7$.
19. 0
20. 271.4
21. .583
22. .083
23. 2,300,000
24. 2510
25. Answers may vary. sample: the active cell is the one which takes the information being typed; it is highlighted.
26. a. $\frac{1}{4}$ b. $\frac{11}{36}$ c. No

Quiz   Lessons 8–1 Through 8–3

1.–3.
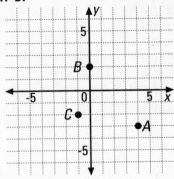

4. IV
5. exercise walking, swimming, aerobic exercising
6. 5, percent of population 7 years and over
7. Answers may vary. sample: It is easier to make comparisons from a graph than from a table.

25. a.
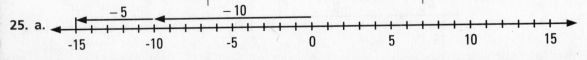

1. sample points:
(0, 3), (2, 1), (-2, 5)

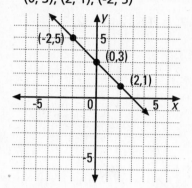

2. a.–c.

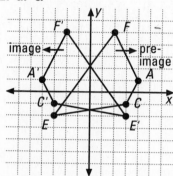

d. *y*-axis

3. Yes. △*ABC* can be rotated and translated to correspond with △*PQR*. They have the same size and shape and are therefore congruent.

4. The figure is moved up 2 units.

Chapter 8 Test, Form A

1. Answers will vary. sample: (i) to show trends; (ii) to show a lot of information in a small space

2. 121.1 million

3. (b)

4. 5 | 4
6 | 1 7 3
7 | 9 8 7 1 0 2 5 8
8 | 6 7 0 8 4
9 | 4 3 3 3

5. a. 40   **b.** 78   **c.** 93

6.

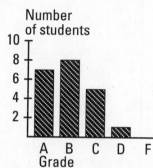

7. False

8. 80 million bicycles or automobiles

9. about 60 million

10. 1988; about 67 million

11.

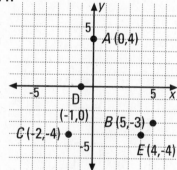

12. sample points:
(-2, -1), (0, 1), (2, 3)

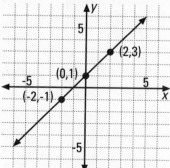

13.

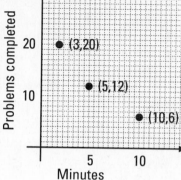

14. a.

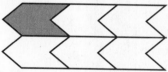

b.

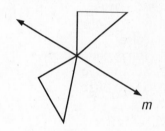

15. sample:

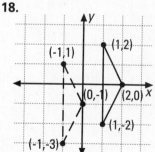

16.

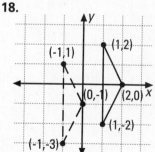

17. a. (-1, 1)   **b.** (0, -1)
c. (-1, -3)

18.

19. translation
20. a. 90°   **b.** 9

ANSWERS

201

ANSWERS

1. Answers will vary. sample:
   (i) It is easier to understand than tables or prose writing.
   (ii) It shows trends easily.

2. about 25,000 BTUs

3. (a)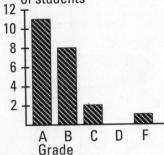

4. 4 | 9
    5 |
    6 | 5 3
    7 | 2 5 9
    8 | 1 8 8 5 4 3 6 4 1
    9 | 5 6 2 2 7 6
   10 | 0

5. a. 51   b. 84.5   c. 81, 84, 88, 92, 96

6. Number of students

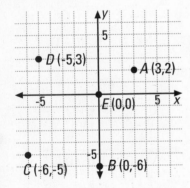

7. False

8. 100 lb consumed

9. about 45 lb

10. about 50 lb

11.

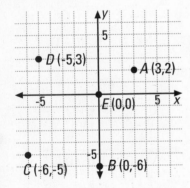

12. sample points:
   (−2, 6), (0, 4), (2, 2)

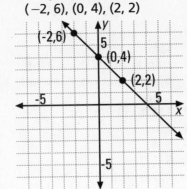

13.

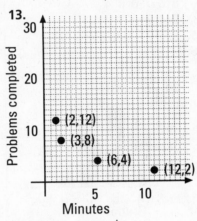

14. a.

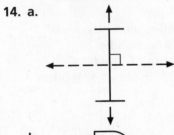

   b.

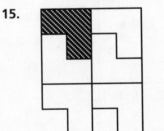

15.

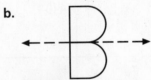

16.

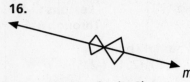

17. a. (3, 1)   b. (2, 3)
    c. (0, -2)

18.

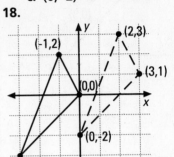

19. translation

20. a. 90°   b. 12

**Chapter 8 Test,
Cumulative Form**

1. Dubuque, Iowa
2. 30 feet
3. Dubuque, Quad Cities, St. Louis
4.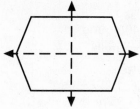
5. square
6. (2, -4)
7. a. III   b. (-1, -1)
8.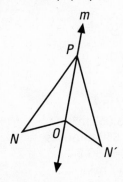
9.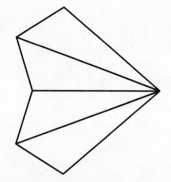
10. sample points: (-3, -6), (0, -3), (3, 0)
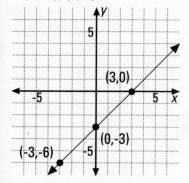

11. 3
12. -y
13. $x = -\frac{61}{8}$
14. $x = 20$
15. $x = 37$
16. 30 in.
17. $n^2 - 6$
18. 4070.1 g
19. 90
20. $1\frac{39}{40}$
21. 8.125
22. .000001
23. a. 70°   b. 20°
24. March
25. Answers may vary. sample: Both prices were fairly steady in January, declined at the end of February, rose from March through June, declined in June, and rose again at the end of June. The price of silver rose more sharply from March to June than the price of gold did.

Quiz   **Lessons 9–1
Through 9–4**

1. a. 3.5 m   b. 7500 cm²
2. a. 5x ft²   b. 10x ft³
3. (d)
4. (a)
5. (b)
6. (c)
7. $\frac{8}{45}$
8. $\frac{40}{7}$
9. 1
10. $\frac{5}{8}$
11. 2
12. $\frac{8}{3}$
13. $\frac{2}{5}$

14.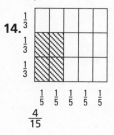

$\frac{4}{15}$

Quiz   **Lessons 9–5
Through 9–8**

1. 6295.38 hours
2. ab
3. 38
4. no solution
5. $x = 0$
6. (c)
7.-8.

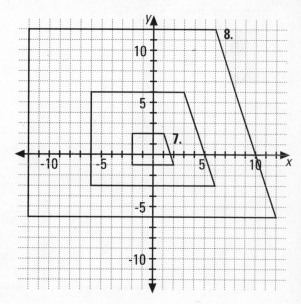

ANSWERS

203

Chapter 9 Test, Form A

1. 33.15 cm^2
2. Associative Property of Multiplication
3. $\frac{1}{6}$
4. $\frac{1}{216}$
5. 7.375¢ per ounce
6. $\frac{1}{2.54}$ in./cm
7. False
8. (3, -6)
9. $14.63/hr
10. expansion
11. $\frac{3}{10}$
12. 1
13. $\frac{5}{6}$
14. -8
15. 210
16. -125
17. 0
18. 7.5 sq in.
19. 100 mm^3
20. 12 pints
21. $A = 96$
22. 96 in.^{3}
23. $\frac{1}{32}$
24. a.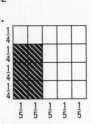
b. $\frac{6}{20}$

25. 63,360 in.
26. a. See below.
    b. 10   c. =   d. similar
27. Answers may vary. sample: Use the Commutative Property followed by the Associative Property: 5 × 100 × 2 = 100 × (5 × 2) = 100 × 10 = 1000. Then 1.8 × 1000 = 1800.

Chapter 9 Test, Form B

1. 32.24 cm^2
2. Commutative Property of Multiplication
3. $\frac{1}{9}$
4. $\frac{1}{1296}$
5. $.40/pound
6. $\frac{1}{2.2}$ km/lb
7. False
8. (-.6, 1.2)
9. $15.38/hr
10. contraction
11. $\frac{5}{27}$
12. 1
13. $\frac{5}{4}$, or $1\frac{1}{4}$
14. -60
15. 3360
16. 256
17. -36
18. 147 in.^{2}
19. 265.05 cm^3
20. 44,650 minutes
21. $A = 150$
22. ≈ .47 m^3
23. $\frac{81}{256}$
24. a.
b. $\frac{2}{35}$

26. a.

25. 65 L

26. a. See below.
b. 15 **c.** = **d.** similar

27. Answers may vary.
sample: .125 and .25 can
be written as $\frac{1}{8}$ and $\frac{1}{4}$
respectively. The problem
becomes $8 \times 4 \times \frac{1}{8} \times \frac{1}{4}$,
which becomes $(8 \times \frac{1}{8}) \times (4 \times \frac{1}{4})$ using the
Commutative Property of
Multiplication. This equals
1×1, which is 1, using
the Property of Reciprocals.

**Chapter 9 Test,
Cumulative Form**

1. 8.74 m²
2. $\frac{2}{5}$ or .4
3. 14.1¢
4. False
5. 3
6. $\frac{5}{16}$
7. $-\frac{11}{12}$
8. 34.8
9. 16
10. 0
11. 11,520 in.³
12. $\frac{1}{1024}$
13. 39,283.2 in.
14. **a.**   **b.** $\frac{2}{15}$

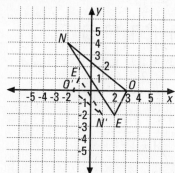

15. **a.**

b. =
c. Answers may vary.
sample: (0, 0)

16. (b); (a); (b); (c); (d)
17. False
18. sample: A
19. 14 cm
20. 1000
21. $2,480,000,000
22. 3.125
23. .0000003
24. 75
25. 12
26.

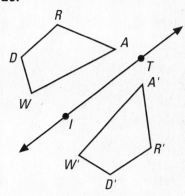

27. sample points: (-3, -4),
(0, -1), (3, 2)

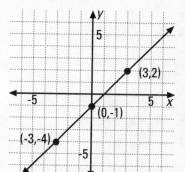

28. **a.** about 28% **b.** 35–44
years old **c.** 16
29. $x = -8.9$
30. 13
31. No. Explanations may
vary.
sample: Consider the
numbers 4 and 7.
$4 \div 7 \neq 7 \div 4$

26. a.

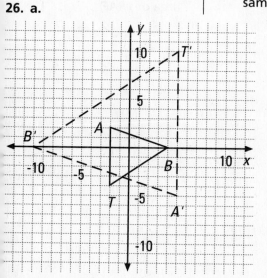

Comprehensive Test, Chapters 1–9

1. (a)
2. (b)
3. (d)
4. (b)
5. (b)
6. (d)
7. (d)
8. (a)
9. (c)
10. (c)
11. (d)
12. (a)
13. (a)
14. (c)
15. (a)
16. (c)
17. (b)
18. (c)
19. (a)
20. (a)
21. (b)
22. (a)
23. (b)
24. (c)
25. (a)
26.

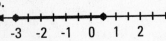

27. 3,186,560
28. 16,368 feet
29. a. $\frac{5}{18}$ b. $\frac{1}{9}$
30. $x = a - b - c$
31. 4 and 6
32. sample:

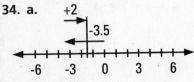

33. a. 90° b. 50° c. 140°
    d. 40°
34. a.

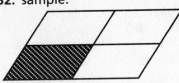

    b. -1.5
35. 911 lb
36. The Additive Identity is
    zero. The Multiplicative
    Identity is 1. When zero is
    added to a number or the
    number is multiplied by
    1, that number keeps its
    identity.

ANSWERS

Quiz — Lessons 10–1 Through 10–4

1. $\frac{1}{2}f$
2. $(-3) + (-3) + (-3) + (-3)$
3. $P = 8n$
4. -4
5. $12x + 3y$
6. $D = \frac{4}{5}$
7. $-1\frac{1}{3}$
8. a. $3x = 180°$ b. $x = 60°$
9. a. $.019x = 168$
   b. $x \approx 8{,}842$ books

Quiz — Lessons 10–5 Through 10–7

1. multiplication
2. 6
3. $M = -6\frac{10}{41}$
4. $L = -20$
5. 70
6. $8.5x + 11y$
7. 544 in.²
8.

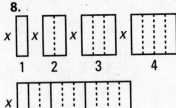

$1 + 2 + 3 + 4$

Chapter 10 Test, Form A

1. $4k + 6j$
2. $5b$
3. $6 \cdot \frac{1}{2}$
4. $7x$
5. $-\frac{1}{4}$
6. square feet
7. $\frac{1}{2}ab$
8. 6 square units
9. 18 square units
10. 36 square units
11. $x = 220$
12. $t = \frac{14}{55}$
13. $c = 100$
14. $y = 2$
15. a. 34,225 ft²   b. 1136 ft
    c. square feet
16. $2w + 4 = 9$
17. $\$11.98 \times 4$
    $= 4(\$12.00 - \$0.02)$
    $= 4 \cdot \$12.00 - 4 \cdot \$0.02$
    $= \$48.00 - \$0.08$
    $= \$47.92$
18. $7(3m + y) = 7 \cdot 3m + 7y$
19. $\$30{,}680$
20. 1755 cm²
21. Calculate the area of
    TRAP, using the formula
    $A = \frac{1}{2}b(h_1 + h_2)$.
    Calculate the areas of
    TRA and TAP using the
    formula $A = \frac{1}{2}bh$.
    Add the areas of TRA and
    TAP. Compare with the
    area of TRAP.

Chapter 10 Test, Form B

1. $3a + 2b - 5d$
2. $7.34b$
3. $6 \times \frac{2}{5}$
4. $3ab$
5. $-\frac{1}{7.2}$
6. square miles
7. $2a^2$ square units
8. 30 square units
9. 54 square units
10. 120 square units
11. $z = -17$
12. $M = \frac{4}{33}$
13. $F = 98\frac{3}{5}$
14. $y = -3$
15. a. 2500 cm^2 b. 40 cm
    c. square cm
16. $4w + 4 = 7$
17. $\$9.98 \times 5$
    $= 5\,(\$10.00 - \$0.02)$
    $= 5 \cdot \$10.00 - 5 \cdot \$0.02$
    $= \$50.00 - \$0.10$
    $= \$49.90$
18.

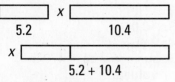

19. 1.3 hr or 78 minutes
20. Yes. The surface area of the box is 576 in.² The area of the newspaper is 613.125 in.²
21. Calculate the area of *TRAP* using the formula $A = \frac{1}{2}b(h_1 + h_2)$. Calculate the areas of *TRA* and *TAP* using the formula $A = \frac{1}{2}bh$. Add the areas of *TRA* and *TAP*. Compare with the area of *TRAP*.

Chapter 10 Test, Cumulative Form

1. $y = 144$
2. $m = -4$
3. $t = 32$
4. $m = \frac{p}{n}$
5. $y = -17.5$
6. $4a + 3b$
7. $\frac{m}{3}$
8. $-4x$
9. $160 + 8t + 8n$
10. -12
11. $-80y$
12. $.3\overline{8}$
13. 420 square units
14. $.58b$
15. 147 square units
16. 2250 cm^2
17. 9000 cm^3
18. 2
19. 3
20. a. volume   b. weight
    c. volume
21. Answers may vary. sample:

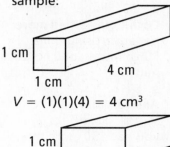

$V = (1)(1)(4) = 4 \text{ cm}^3$

$V = (1)(2)(2) = 4 \text{ cm}^3$
22. $(-2.5, -1.5)$
23. $-\frac{1}{2}$
24. 35%
25. $750
26. shorter
27. 33.2
28. 9.870
29. about 5,501,333 cars
30. about 2 million

Quiz   Lessons 11–1 Through 11–4

1. 2
2. 8
3. -4
4. -21
5. positive
6. $79 = 15 \cdot 5 + 4$
7. $\frac{h}{d}$
8. 3 miles 2860 feet
9. store B is cheaper

Quiz   Lessons 11–5 Through 11–8

1. $\frac{329}{412}, \frac{412}{329}$
2. $17t$
3. $K \cdot N = L \cdot M$
4. (b)
5. 4.5 cm
6. $x = 5.\overline{7}$, or $5\frac{7}{9}$
7. $y = 12.5$
8. 3.8%
9. 19.5

Chapter 11 Test, Form A

1. $31 = 7 \cdot 4 + 3$
2. $\dfrac{d}{p}$
3. $\dfrac{1}{2} \cdot \dfrac{4}{3}$
4. (c)
5. 200%
6. 66
7. t and 11
8. 2 cm, 2.5 cm, and 3 cm
9. 66.2
10. 1.5%
11. They are reciprocals. The answer to Question 9 is c/w. The answer to Question 10 is w/c.
12. $\dfrac{6}{5}$
13. $\dfrac{56}{81}$
14. $-\dfrac{3}{2}$
15. $2\dfrac{1}{2}$
16. $a = 4.8$
17. 65 feet 7.5 inches
18. 5,736,407 pieces of mail per post office
19. Ford earned more per dollar spent on advertising.
20. $2\dfrac{1}{6}$ hours, or 2 hours 10 min
21. a. 3.45   b. 10
22. Answers may vary. sample: Bob lost 15 lb. Mary lost 5 lb. Fill in the blank: Bob lost _____ times as much as Mary lost.

Chapter 11 Test, Form B

1. $67 = 9 \cdot 7 + 4$
2. $\dfrac{\$12.50}{p}$
3. $\dfrac{2}{3} \cdot \dfrac{4}{1}$
4. (a)
5. 400%
6. $3x$
7. 5 and x
8. 6 cm, 8 cm, and 10 cm
9. 1.6
10. 61.6%
11. They are reciprocals, since the answer to Question 9 is c/w and the answer to Question 10 is w/c.
12. $\dfrac{1}{6}$
13. $\dfrac{44}{21}$, or $2\dfrac{2}{21}$
14. -1.5, or $-\dfrac{3}{2}$
15. $\dfrac{2}{3}$
16. $b = 5$
17. 164 feet and .5 inch
18. 3.7 $2 bills per person
19. Coca-Cola earned more per advertising dollar.
20. 508 minutes, or 8 hrs 28 min
21. a. .6   b. 7.2
22. Answers may vary. sample: Six weeks ago you had $30 more than you do now. Find the average loss per year.

Chapter 11 Test, Cumulative Form

1. $\dfrac{c}{r}$
2. 3×2
3. 125%
4. $11m$
5. (a)
6. 53.2%
7. $\dfrac{4}{5}$
8. $\dfrac{25}{8}$, or $3\dfrac{1}{8}$
9. $-\dfrac{8}{5}$, or $-1\dfrac{3}{5}$
10. 4
11. $s = 11$
12. $T = 7.5$
13. 127 feet 3 inches
14. about 34.5 mph
15. Answers may vary. sample: A loss of $10 is _____ times as much as a loss of $5.
16. 63 calories
17. $5p - 4q$
18. $3x + xy$
19. (a)
20. 4 feet
21. $\dfrac{2}{3}$
22. 2
23. 10,000
24. 2.46×10^8
25. surface area = 472 in.^{2} volume = 560 in.^{3}
26. $x = \dfrac{2}{3}$
27. $99 \cdot 54 = (100 - 1)\,54 = (100)(54) - (1)(54) = 5400 - 54 = 5346$
28. $5625
29. 1
30.

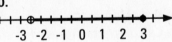

ANSWERS

Quiz   **Lessons 12–1**
                      Through 12–3

1. sample: $\frac{31}{5}$
2. (b)
3. radical sign
4. 8.7
5. hypotenuse
6. False
7. $\frac{8}{11}$
8. 14
9. 10
10. 3
11. 127.3 ft
12. 8 feet

Quiz   **Lessons 12–4**
                      Through 12–7

1. $C = 2\pi r$
2. True
3. (c)
4. $\frac{1}{3}$
5. surface area
6. volume
7. **a.** 377 cm^2 **b.** 603 cm^2
   c. 1130 cm^3
8. sample:

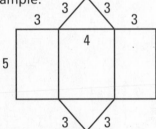

9. about 78.5 feet
10. about 490.9 ft^2
11. about 1472.6 ft^3

Chapter 12 Test, Form A

1. (b)
2. 8 and 9
3. 5 and -5
4. $\sqrt{60}$ cm
5. $d = 2r$
6. $\frac{1}{6}$
7. right triangle
8. sample: $\frac{-23}{4}$
9. $\frac{7}{90}$
10. $\frac{214}{33}$
11. $b = 28$
12. $\sqrt{85}$
13. 129 feet
14. 72 mm
15. **a.** Leon
  b. Fiona 's pizzas: $A = 5 \cdot \pi \cdot (3.5)^2 \approx 192.4$ in.^{2}
  Leon's pizza: $A = \pi \cdot 8^2 \approx 201.1$ in.^{2}
16. 50 in.^{2}
17. 180 square units
18. 90 cubic units
19. **a.** No, because the ends are open.
  b. 1,010,000 ft^2
20. 2,660,000 ft^3
21. 178,000 ft^3
22. about 12,164 ft^2

Chapter 12 Test, Form B

1. (a)
2. 10 and 11
3. 7 and -7
4. $\sqrt{14}$ cm
5. $C = 2\pi r$
6. $\frac{1}{3}$
7. False
8. sample: $\frac{-17}{4}$
9. $\frac{1}{450}$
10. $\frac{268}{33}$
11. $c = 2$
12. $b = \sqrt{3}$
13. Yes. The diagonal of the card is about 100.7 mm.
14. 57 mm
15. **a.** 580,000,000 miles
  b. about 2.7×10^{16} mi^2
16. about 5.3×10^{14} mi^2
17. 180 square units
18. 135 square units
19. **a.** No, because the ends are open.
  b. 53,080,000 ft^2
20. 53,080,000 ft^3
21. 11.9 in.^{3}
22. 15.9 in.^{2}

Chapter 12 Test, Cumulative Form

1. (c)
2. $\frac{157}{25}$
3. -9
4. 1.77
5. 135°
6. $\sqrt{8}$ ft
7. $\frac{6}{11}$
8. $\sqrt{18}$, or ≈ 4.2, in.
9. about 6.6 ft
10. about 15.7 in.
11. about 19.6 in.²
12. about 3.3 in.²
13. about 5.4 cm.³
14. about 31.9 cm²
15. 87,000,000 km²
16. 76,898,000,000 km³
17. A rational number can be written as the ratio of two integers. An irrational number cannot.
18. 2
19. 23 cents per minute
20. -5
21. $4m - 2n$
22. $k = -1$
23. 4
24. (c) and (d)
25. $6\frac{12}{13}$, or ≈ 6.9, units
26. 19 seasons

Quiz Lessons 13–1 Through 13–4

1. $y = 2$
2. a.

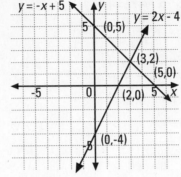

   b. (3, 2)
3. a.

H

   b. Answers may vary. sample: yes, because the number of heads is close to $\frac{1}{2}$ of the number of tosses

Chapter 13 Test, Form A

1. $a = \frac{1}{2}$
2. $b = 1$
3.-4.

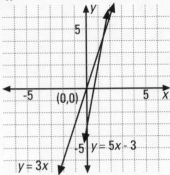

5. Find the point where the lines intersect. The x-coordinate of that point, which appears to be 1.5, is the solution to the equation.
6. 3
7. sample: -13.8 and -13.2
8. a. (c) b. 5
9. a. Jeong: $s = 40 + 3w$; Heewon: $s = 32 + 5w$
   b. $40 + 3w = 32 + 5w$
   c. $w = 4$
10. a. step 3 b. $x = -\frac{1}{2}$
11.

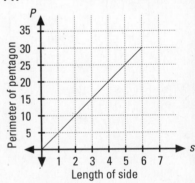

12. a. 15 cm b. (3, 15)
13. The values of s and P cannot be negative.

ANSWERS

14. a. Sample: $\frac{4}{6}$, $\frac{6}{9}$, $\frac{-2}{-3}$, $\frac{-6}{-9}$

b. See below.

c. $a = \frac{2}{3}b$

15. a.

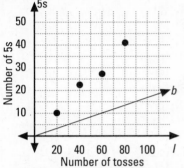

Number of 5s vs Number of tosses

b. No, the data should be closer to the solid line drawn above.

1. $r = 9\frac{6}{11}$, or $\frac{105}{11}$

2. $y = -\frac{3}{2}$

3.-4.

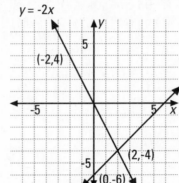

$y = -2x$
$(-2,4)$
$(2,-4)$
$(0,-6)$
$y = x - 6$

5. Find the point where the lines intersect. The x-coordinate of that point, which appears to be 2, is the solution to the equation.

6. 1

7. sample: -5.7 and -5.2

8. a. (a) **b.** 4

9. a. car A: $d = 100 - 50t$, car B: $d = 20 + 40t$

b. $100 - 50t = 20 + 40t$

c. $t = \frac{8}{9}$ hours

10. a. step 3 **b.** $x = -\frac{1}{4}$

11.

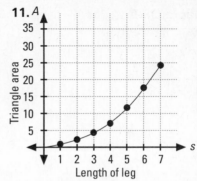

Triangle area vs Length of leg

12. a. 8 cm² **b.** (4, 8)

13. The legs cannot have negative lengths.

14. a. sample: $\frac{-6}{4}$, $\frac{-9}{6}$, $\frac{6}{-4}$, $\frac{9}{-6}$

b. See below.

c. $a = \frac{-3}{2}b$

15. a.

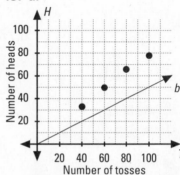

Number of heads vs Number of tosses

b. No. You would expect the data to be closer to the solid line drawn above.

ANSWERS

14. b.

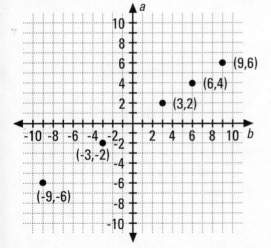

(9,6), (6,4), (3,2), (-3,-2), (-9,-6)

14. b.

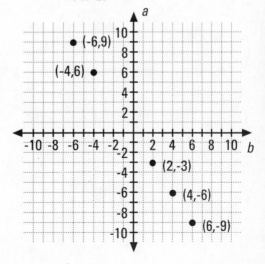

(-6,9), (-4,6), (2,-3), (4,-6), (6,-9)

211

Chapter 13 Test, Cumulative Form

1. $k = -2$
2. $r = \frac{-9}{2}$, or $-4\frac{1}{2}$
3. $x = -8$
4. a.

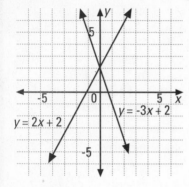

$y = 2x + 2$ $y = -3x + 2$

   b. $(0, 2)$
5. a. Raphael: $h = 140 + 3t$,
      Juana: $h = 150 + t$
   b. $140 + 3t = 150 + t$
   c. $t = 5$ years
6. a. sample: $\frac{-6}{10}$, $\frac{3}{-5}$, $\frac{6}{-10}$
   b. See below
   c. $a = \frac{-3}{5}b$
7. (c)
8. 26
9. -1
10. 3
11. (a)

12. (d)
13. $\frac{47}{45}$
14. $\frac{47}{165}$
15. $c = \sqrt{50}$
16. $a = 5$
17. 87.96 cm^2
18. 62.83 cm^3
19. 9 and 10
20. $\frac{24}{5}$, or $4\frac{4}{5}$
21. $46 = 7 \cdot 6 + 4$
22. $4n - 6$
23. $\frac{9}{20}$
24. $\frac{11}{20}$
25. 8

Comprehensive Test, Chapters 1–13

1. (a)
2. (b)
3. (d)
4. (c)
5. (a)
6. (a)
7. (c)
8. (c)
9. (a)
10. (c)
11. (d)
12. (c)
13. (d)
14. (c)
15. (b)
16. (c)
17. (d)
18. (b)
19. (c)
20. (d)
21. (a)
22. (a)
23. (b)
24. (c)
25. (b)
26. $x = 9$
27. $t = 1$
28. 5
29. a. Sample : 3.8 (EE) $8 \div 2$
      (EE) 8 (+/−) (=)
   b. 19,000,000,000,000,000
30. $\sqrt{50}$ feet
31. a. 52° b. 90° c. 38°
   d. 142°
32. 280 in.^{2}
33. 1.9 miles
34. 120 students
35.

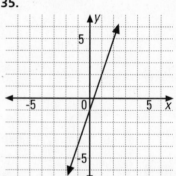

6. b.

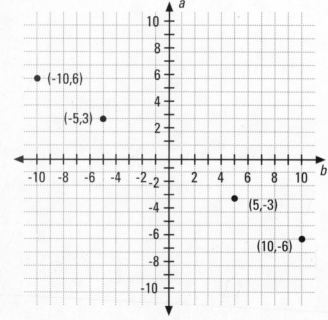

212

1. Use your calculator. Determine a way to fill in the boxes below with the digits 5, 6, 7, 8, 9, and 0 to make a product that is between 30 and 40. (You may use each digit only once.) What is your product?

☐ . ☐ ☐   X   ☐ ☐ . ☐

Objectives C, E

☐ Understands the comparing and ordering of decimals.

☐ Demonstrates an ability to use a calculator to perform arithmetic operations.

☐ Identifies an appropriate multiplication, such as 0.57×68.9 or 0.58×67.9.

☐ Gives the correct product, such as 39.273 or 39.382.

2. Describe a real situation in which it is appropriate to round a decimal *up* and a different situation when it is appropriate to round a decimal *down*. Give specific examples to show how you would round the decimals involved.

Objectives D, K

☐ Can round decimals up or down to the nearest value of a decimal place.

☐ Is able to deal with estimates in real situations.

☐ Describes two real situations such as pricing and determining safe cargo weights.

☐ Gives appropriate examples such as: if 3 pens cost $5, 1 will cost $1.67; if an elevator can safely carry 2350 lb, 2300 lb is a safer weight than is 2400 lb.

3. Make a drawing to show why the following statement is true.

$$\frac{2}{3} = \frac{4}{6} = \frac{6}{9}$$

Objective J

☐ Demonstrates an understanding of the Equal Fractions Property.

☐ Makes an appropriate drawing such as:

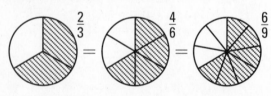

4. What numbers do you think are represented by points *A* and *B* on the number line below? Explain your reasoning.

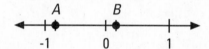

Objective M

☐ Demonstrates an ability to read numbers on a number line.

☐ Gives reasonable estimates for the numbers represented by *A* and *B*, such as $-\frac{5}{6}$ and $\frac{1}{6}$.

☐ Gives an appropriate explanation.

5. Explain why the decimals 0.16, $0.1\overline{6}$, and $0.\overline{16}$ are not equal to the same number. Then use these three decimals to fill in the blanks in the following expression.

_____ > _____ > _____

Objectives B, H, I

☐ Demonstrates an understanding of the raised bar symbol for repeating decimals.

☐ Demonstrates an understanding of the > symbol for ordering decimals.

☐ Gives an appropriate explanation.

☐ Gives $0.1\overline{6} > 0.\overline{16} > 0.16$ as the correct order.

6. Your friend was absent from school for a few days and has asked you to explain how to convert fractions and mixed numbers to decimals. How would you explain what to do? Tell your friend about the decimals and fractions you should know from memory.

Objectives F, G

☐ Can convert simple fractions and mixed numbers to decimals by dividing the fraction's numerator by its denominator.

☐ Demonstrates a knowledge of common decimals and fractions between 0 and 1.

☐ Gives an appropriate explanation.

EVALUATION GUIDES

Teacher Notes

Objectives B, C, D, E, K

Concepts and Skills This activity requires students to:
- use a calculator to perform arithmetic operations.
- make decisions based on given data and real-life experiences.
- compare, round, add, subtract, multiply, and divide decimals.
- estimate sums, differences, products, and quotients of decimals.
- use data from a table.
- summarize results.

Guiding Questions
- How can you estimate a single cost when you are given a range of costs?
- Do you think there are other expenses that your family should consider? What are they? What do you think they will cost?

Answers
a. O) $22.44-$44.88; W) $17.38-$34.76; SF) $28.86-$57.72
b. O) ≈ 62 gal, $61.38-$73.78; W) ≈ 48 gal, $47.52-$57.12; SF) ≈ 80 gal, $79.20-$95.20
c. Budget totals should include costs for tolls and gasoline as well as $1120-$1470 for hotel/motel, $840-$1120 for food, and additional costs for admission fees.
d. Answers will vary.

Extension
Have students choose a vacation destination and research its distance from your city or town and current information about the cost of traveling to that city. Have the students prepare budgets based on these costs and on the number of people in their own families. Have them do further research to compare the cost of traveling to that city using the family car to the cost of traveling by plane, train, or bus and renting a car at their destination.

Evaluation

Level	Standard to be achieved for performance at specified level
5	The student prepares a written budget that is neat, accurate, thorough, and somewhat imaginative. The student makes reasonable estimates and, based on those estimates, all costs are calculated completely and accurately. The student interprets the results intelligently and makes a reasonable estimate of the amount to be saved each month.
4	The student prepares a written budget that is complete and easy to read. The student understands how to make estimates and perform operations with them, but may make minor errors in rounding or calculation. The student interprets the results intelligently and makes a reasonable estimate of the amount to be saved each month.
3	The student is able to prepare a written budget that is reasonably complete, but may need help in getting started. The student understands how to make estimates and perform operations with them, but there may be major errors or omissions in rounding and calculation. The student may have difficulty identifying an amount to be saved each month.
2	The student attempts to create a written budget, but it is disorganized and incomplete. The student understands that the situation involves estimation and can make some simple estimates, such as an estimate of the total distance involved. However, the student becomes confused and cannot make estimates that involve two steps, such as an estimate of the cost of gasoline.
1	The student makes little if any attempt to prepare a written budget or to identify an amount to be saved each month. Responses reflect little understanding of the situation. Even when prompted, the student is unable to make any reasonable estimates or meaningful calculations.

1. Explain the differences among these three expressions.

$$2 \times 10 \qquad 2^{10} \qquad 10^2$$

Objectives A, C, D

☐ Demonstrates an ability to multiply by 10, 100, 1000, and so on.
☐ Is able to convert powers to decimals.
☐ Can give decimals for integer powers of 10.
☐ Recognizes that $2 \times 10 = 20$, $2^{10} = 1024$, and $10^2 = 100$.

2. Suppose that the ⓪ key of your calculator is broken. How could you use the scientific notation key to display this number?

1850000

Objectives F, L, N

☐ Understands scientific notation.
☐ Demonstrates an ability to use the scientific notation key on a calculator.
☐ Gives an appropriate method for entering the number, such as entering this key sequence: 1.85 ⌊EE⌋7

3. Explain why this number is *not* written in scientific notation.

$$47 \times 10^{-5}$$

What is the correct scientific notation for the number?

Objectives F, L, N

☐ Understands scientific notation.
☐ Demonstrates an ability to write numbers in scientific notation.
☐ Identifies 4.7×10^{-4} as the correct notation.
☐ Gives a logical explanation.

4. Let n represent an amount of money. List the amounts that follow in order from least to greatest. Explain your reasoning.

$$n \qquad 7.5\% \text{ of } n \qquad 75\% \text{ of } n \qquad 750\% \text{ of } n$$

Objectives G, K, M

☐ Demonstrates an understanding of the Substitution Principle.
☐ Can find percents of quantities.
☐ Gives 7.5% of n, 75% of n, n, 750% of n as the correct order.
☐ Gives a logical explanation.

5. Carla made this graph to show how she plans to use the $585 that she received as graduation gifts. About how much does she plan to spend on each item?

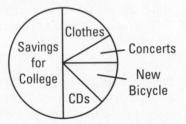

Objective O

☐ Is able to interpret circle graphs.
☐ Gives a reasonable estimate for each item: Savings, $292; Clothes, $98; Concerts, $49; Bicycle, $73; CDs, $73

6. Explain why each step shown below is true.

Step 1 $5\frac{1}{4}\% = 5.25\%$

Step 2 $= 5.25 \times 0.01$

Step 3 $= 0.0525$

Objectives E, G, H

☐ Recognizes common fraction and percent equivalents.
☐ Demonstrates an ability to multiply by 0.1, 0.01, 0.001, and so on.
☐ Can convert percents to decimals.
☐ Gives an appropriate reason for each step:
Step 1: Substitution Principle
Step 2: Meaning of percent
Step 3: Arithmetic

Teacher Notes

Objectives G, H, I, J, K, M, O

Concepts and Skills This activity requires students to:
- read, interpret, and analyze data presented in a circle graph.
- make decisions concerning the appropriate presentation of data.
- convert among fractions, decimals, percents.
- operate with fractions and percents as decimals.
- find percents of quantities.
- summarize results.

Guiding Questions
- Why is it important that all three graphs be labeled in the same way?
- How can you use what you know about circle graphs to check your calculations?

Answers
a., e. Answers will vary.

b. Grade 6 sectors: W) 72, 20%; C) 108, 30%; B) 18, 5%; SB) 144, 40%; PT) 18, 5%

Grade 7 sectors: W) $\frac{1}{4}$, 75; C) $\frac{1}{5}$, 60; B) $\frac{2}{25}$, 24; SB) $\frac{7}{20}$, 105; PT) $\frac{3}{25}$, 36

Grade 8 sectors: W) $\frac{3}{10}$, 30%; C) $\frac{3}{20}$, 15%; B) $\frac{1}{8}$, $12\frac{1}{2}$%; SB) $\frac{1}{4}$, 25%; PT) $\frac{7}{40}$, $17\frac{1}{2}$%

c. 219 students; $\frac{219}{900}$, or $\frac{73}{300}$; $\approx 24\%$

d.

Gr.	W	C	B	SB	PT
6	72	108	18	144	18
7	75	60	24	105	36
8	72	36	30	60	42
Stud. Totals	219	204	72	309	96
Fractions	$\frac{219}{900}$	$\frac{204}{900}$	$\frac{72}{900}$	$\frac{309}{900}$	$\frac{96}{900}$
Percents	24%	23%	8%	34%	11%

Extension
Have students devise a survey and use it to collect data about the methods of transportation used by students in your school. Students should organize their data and compare it to the Springfield Middle School data. Have them propose reasons for any significant differences between the sets of data.

Evaluation

Standard to be achieved for
Level performance at specified level

5 The student demonstrates a clear understanding of the relationships among fractions, decimals, and percents, and all calculations are accurate and complete. The student interprets the data reasonably and makes at least three sound observations regarding trends in data. The graphs and the report are neat, thorough, and easy to read.

4 The student demonstrates a clear understanding of the relationships among fractions, decimals, and percents, but may make minor errors in calculations. The student interprets the data reasonably and makes several sound observations. The graphs and the report are neat and easy to read, but they may lack some detail.

3 There is a fundamental understanding of the relationships among fractions, decimals, and percents, but there may be one or more major errors or omissions in the student's work. The student is able to make an appropriate choice for labeling the graphs and can identify one or two trends in the data, but may need assistance getting started. The graphs and the report may contain significant errors.

2 The student demonstrates some understanding of the relationships among fractions, decimals, and percents, but is only able to convert among and operate with them with a great deal of assistance. The student is able to make an appropriate choice for labeling the graphs and can identify one or two trends in the data, but may need considerable prompting throughout the process. The student prepares the graphs and a report, but they are disorganized, inaccurate, and incomplete.

1 The student displays little understanding of fractions, decimals, percents, and the relationships among them. The student may attempt some calculations, but they are inappropriate and incorrect. There is no evidence that the student understands the given data, and there is no meaningful attempt to adjust the graphs or identify trends. Attempts at communication are jumbled and irrelevant.

1. Use a ruler to draw a line segment that satisfies the following conditions:

   To the nearest inch, its length is 3 in.

   To the nearest half inch, its length is $3\frac{1}{2}$ in.

   Now find the length of your segment to the nearest *millimeter.*

Objectives A, K

- ☐ Is able to measure lengths using the U.S. system of measurement.
- ☐ Demonstrates an ability to measure lengths using the metric system of measurement.
- ☐ Draws a segment that measures more than 3 in. and less than or equal to $3\frac{1}{2}$ in.
- ☐ Gives the metric measure as greater than 76 mm and less than or equal to 88 mm.

2. You know that the area of a square is between 16 mm^2 and 36 mm^2. What do you know about the length of one side of this square?

   This same square is one of the six faces of a cube. What do you know about the volume of the cube?

Objective D

- ☐ Is able to find the area of a square.
- ☐ Is able to find the volume of a cube.
- ☐ Correctly identifies the length of one side of the square as between 4 mm and 6 mm.
- ☐ Correctly identifies the volume of the cube as between 64 mm^3 and 216 mm^3.

3. Your recipe for banana milkshakes requires 750 mL of milk. You want to triple the recipe, and you have a half gallon of milk in the refrigerator. Is this enough? Explain.

Objectives G, H, I

- ☐ Can convert within the metric and U.S. systems of measurement.
- ☐ Can convert between systems of measurement.
- ☐ Recognizes that a half gallon is not enough.
- ☐ Gives a logical explanation, that 1893 mL is less than 3 × 750, or 2250, mL.

4. Without using a protractor, draw an obtuse angle. Label it $\angle RST$. Tell how you know that $\angle RST$ is obtuse. Then use your protractor to find m$\angle RST$.

Objectives B, C

- ☐ Demonstrates an ability to distinguish among acute, right, and obtuse angles by sight.
- ☐ Is able to measure angles using a protractor.
- ☐ Draws an angle with measure between 90° and 180°.
- ☐ Gives a logical explanation.

5. Name something that you would measure in meters and something that you would measure in centimeters. Explain your reasoning.

   If you had to measure the same things using the U.S. system of measurement, what units would you use?

Objective F

- ☐ Is able to choose appropriate units for measuring in the U.S. or metric system of measurement.
- ☐ Names two items, such as fabric and a pen.
- ☐ Gives appropriate units for measuring the items using the U.S. system of measurement.

6. The graph below shows the budget for the town of Midville. Explain how you know that it is drawn incorrectly. Then draw a corrected graph using the given percents.

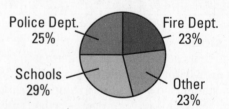

Police Dept. 25%   Fire Dept. 23%

Schools 29%   Other 23%

Objectives L, M

- ☐ Demonstrates an ability to read, make, and interpret circle graphs.
- ☐ Gives a logical explanation.
- ☐ Draws an appropriate graph.

Teacher Notes

Objectives E, F, G, H, I, J

Concepts and Skills This activity requires students to:

- read information from text, a table, and a picture.
- use appropriate units of measure for length, area, volume, capacity, weight, and mass in the U.S. or metric system of measurement.
- convert within the U.S. system and within the metric system of measurement.
- convert between the U.S. system and the metric system of measurement.
- find areas of squares and volumes of cubes.
- add, subtract, multiply, and divide with decimals.
- make a table of results.

Guiding Questions
- What is the best way to keep track of all your calculations?
- To calculate the amount of metal (glass), should you use a unit of length, area, or volume?

Answers
a. No; the volume of the aquarium is only 216 in.^{3}
b.-e. Sample answers are given.
b. A) 6.5 in., 1.2 gal; B) 11 in., 5.8 gal; C) 13 in., 9.5 gal
c. A) 52 in., 211.25 in.^{2}; B) 88 in. 605 in.^{2}; C) 104 in., 845 in.^{2}
d. A) $\approx$ 6 lb, $\approx$ 16 lb; B) $\approx$ 16 lb, $\approx$ 64 lb; C) $\approx$ 22 lb; $\approx$ 101 lb
e. A) 16 cm; B) 28 cm; C) 33 cm

Extension
Give students the additional information that the glass costs $1.79 per square foot and the metal strips cost $.89 per foot, and have them calculate the cost of materials for each aquarium. Students should then propose an appropriate selling price for each aquarium, make reasonable projections for the number of sales of each type of aquarium in the first year of the business, and use these amounts to calculate the amount of profit in that year.

Evaluation

Level	Standard to be achieved for performance at specified level
5	The student demonstrates a clear understanding of measurement and units of measure, and makes reasonable choices for the dimensions of the aquariums. The student has mastered operations with decimals, and all calculations are accurate and complete. The student presents the results in a report that is neat, well-organized, and easy to read.
4	The student demonstrates a clear understanding of measurement and units of measure, and makes reasonable choices for the dimensions of the aquariums. The student performs all necessary calculations, but may make minor errors. The student's report is neat, well-organized, and easy to read, but reflects the minor computational errors.
3	The student demonstrates a fundamental ability to work with measurement and units of measure, but may need some assistance in choosing appropriate dimensions for the aquariums. There may be one or more major errors or omissions in the student's calculations. The student's report reflects these errors, and may be somewhat disorganized.
2	The student demonstrates some understanding of measurement and units of measure, but has a great deal of difficulty in choosing appropriate dimensions for the aquariums. The student needs a considerable amount of assistance in converting units, and there are major errors or omissions in the calculations. The student's report is jumbled and incomplete.
1	The student demonstrates little if any understanding of measurement and units of measure, and, even when prompted, cannot choose reasonable dimensions for the aquariums. The student may perform some calculations, but they are inappropriate to the situation and incomplete. Any attempt at a written report is superfluous or irrelevant.

1. Use each of the numbers and symbols in the box below exactly once. Create a numerical expression whose value is greater than 10 and less than 20. What is the value of your expression?

> 2   ]   5   +   ÷   )
>   \   4   [9
>   •   +   3

Objectives A, D

☐ Understands the correct order of operations.

☐ Is able to use order of operations to evaluate numerical expressions.

☐ Creates an appropriate expression, such as $[2 \times 9 \div 3 + (5 + 4)]$.

☐ Gives 15 as the correct value of the expression.

2. The figure shown below is a rectangle. The formula $A = lw$ gives its area in terms of length and width. Sketch a rectangle that has the same area but a different length and width. Label the length and width.

3 yd

4 ft [rectangle]

Objective I

☐ Can calculate the value of a variable in a formula given the values of other variables in the formula.

☐ Recognizes that the length and width must be given in the same units: 4 ft, 9 ft to give area of 36 ft²; or 3 yd, $1\frac{1}{3}$ yd to give area of 4 yd².

☐ Sketches an appropriate rectangle, such as 12 ft by 3 ft or 2 yd by 2 yd.

3. Identify a real-world pattern that could be described by the variable expression $4n$. Give three instances of the pattern.

Objectives F, G

☐ Describes a real-world pattern using variables, for example, the number of quarts in n gallons is $4n$.

☐ Gives instances of a pattern described with variables: there are 4 qt in 1 gal, 2 • 4 qt in 2 gal, and 3 • 4 qt in 3 gal.

4. Explain the difference between evaluating the algebraic expression $14 - y$ and solving the equation $14 - y = 5$.

Objectives B, C

☐ Demonstrates an understanding of the process of evaluating an algebraic expression.

☐ Demonstrates an understanding of the process of finding solutions to equations.

☐ Gives a logical explanation.

5. Refer to the spinner at the right. Name two different events related to the spinner whose probability is $\frac{1}{3}$.

Explain your reasoning.

Objective J

☐ Can calculate probabilities in a situation with a known number of outcomes.

☐ Names two appropriate events, such as spinning a 3 or an even number.

☐ Gives a logical explanation: There are four 3s (or four even numbers) on the spinner, so the probability is $\frac{4}{12}$, or $\frac{1}{3}$.

6. Name a number graphed on line m that is not graphed on line n. Then name a number graphed on line n that is not graphed on line m.

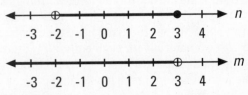

Objective K

☐ Demonstrates an understanding of graphs of inequalities.

☐ Identifies, for example, 3 as being on line n but not on line m, and -3 as being on line m but not on line n.

Teacher Notes

Objectives B, C, G, I

Concepts and Skills This activity requires students to:
- read information from text and a table.
- make decisions based on given data and real-life experiences.
- calculate the value of a variable given the values of other variables in a formula.
- write descriptions of real-world patterns using variables.
- evaluate algebraic expressions.
- find solutions to equations.
- compare and perform operations with decimals.
- prepare a written and graphic summary of results.

Guiding Questions
- How can you work with the prices when some are given as dollars and others are given as cents?
- How does your answer to Part b help in writing an equation for Part c?

Answers
a. $1.60, $2.60, $8.30, $2, 60¢, $1.60, 30¢, 50¢, 30¢
b. $1.60 \cdot 2 = 3.20$, $1.60 \cdot 3 = 4.80$, $1.60 \cdot 4 = 6.40$; $1.60n$
c. $1.60n = 8$; $n = 5$; 5 T-shirts
d. $1.60n = 20$; $n = 12.5$; 12 T-shirts would give $19.20 profit, so 13 is the least number of T-shirts that will yield at least $20 profit.
e. Answers will vary.

Extension
Give students the formula $M = \frac{P}{W} \times 100$, where P is profit, W is wholesale price, and M is percent of markup. Have students estimate the standard percent of markup that was used for items of clothing (about 50%) and for supplies (about 75%). Have them suggest several additional imprint items that might be offered in the bookstore, estimate a wholesale price for each, and use the standard percents of markup to calculate appropriate retail prices.

Evaluation

Level	Standard to be achieved for performance at specified level
5	The student demonstrates a clear understanding of expressions and equations and a keen sense of the given situation. All calculations are accurate and complete. The written report and the graph are thorough, well-organized, and easy to read.
4	The student demonstrates a clear understanding of expressions and equations and a sound grasp of the given situation. The student performs all necessary calculations, but may make some minor errors. The written report and the graph are well-organized and easy to read, but reflect the minor computational errors.
3	The student demonstrates a fundamental understanding of expressions and equations, but may need some assistance in getting started. The student understands the nature of the calculations needed, but there may be one or more major errors or omissions. The written report and the graph reflect these errors, and they may be somewhat disorganized and difficult to read.
2	The student has some understanding of expressions and equations, but can only apply them to the given situation with a great deal of assistance. There are several major errors or omissions in the student's calculations. The student attempts to prepare a written report and a graph, but the results are jumbled and incomplete.
1	The student demonstrates little if any understanding of expressions and equations and, even when prompted, cannot apply them to the given situation. The student attempts some calculations, but they are superfluous or irrelevant. The student may prepare a written report simply by copying the given information, and there is no meaningful effort to draw a graph.

1. Draw a picture to show why the results of these two additions are different.

$$-5 + 7 \qquad 5 + -7$$

2. Write a problem that you can solve with the following equation. Then show how to use the equation to solve your problem.

$$n + 5 = 4$$

Objectives A, M

☐ Understands addition of positive and negative numbers.
☐ Is able to picture addition of positive and negative numbers.
☐ Recognizes that $-5 + 7 = 2$ and $5 + -7 = -2$.
☐ Draws an appropriate picture.

Objectives D, J

☐ Recognizes the Slide Model for Addition.
☐ Can solve equations of the form $x + a = b$.
☐ Writes an appropriate problem, such as: After rising 5°, the temperature was 4°. What was the original temperature?
☐ Shows a correct solution of the problem, -1°.

3. Choose from the fractions in the box below. Find three numbers whose sum is

   a. positive. **b.** negative. **c.** zero.

   Find each sum.

   $$\frac{3}{4} \qquad -\frac{5}{12} \qquad \frac{1}{4} \qquad \frac{1}{3} \qquad -\frac{1}{3} \qquad \frac{1}{12}$$

Objectives A, C

☐ Can add positive and negative numbers.
☐ Applies properties of addition to simplify expressions.
☐ Names three appropriate additions, such as:
a. $\frac{1}{4} + \frac{1}{3} + \frac{1}{12} = \frac{2}{3}$ **b.** $-\frac{1}{3} + \frac{1}{3} + -\frac{5}{12} = -\frac{5}{12}$
c. $\frac{3}{4} + -\frac{5}{12} + -\frac{1}{3} = 0$

4. Use a ruler marked in millimeters to draw a hexagon. Label its vertices and give its name. Then find its perimeter to the nearest millimeter.

Objectives E, H

☐ Draws, labels, and names a hexagon correctly.
☐ Is able to find the perimeter of a polygon.
☐ Gives the correct perimeter of the hexagon.

5. Is the result of a 45° clockwise turn followed by a 135° counterclockwise turn the same as the result of a 135° counterclockwise turn followed by a 45° clockwise turn? What property of addition supports your answer?

6. Each of the 6 faces of a cube is to be labeled with one of the numbers 1, 2, 3, or 4. Tell how to label the faces so that

   a. the probability of rolling a 1 or 2 is $\frac{1}{3}$.

   b. the probability of *not* rolling a 3 is $\frac{2}{3}$.

Objectives F, L

☐ Correctly adds magnitudes of the turns given to get results of 90° and 90°.
☐ Recognizes that the results are the same.
☐ Understands properties of addition.
☐ Identifies the Commutative Property of Addition.

Objectives G, K

☐ Understands mutually exclusive events.
☐ Demonstrates an understanding of the complement of an event.
☐ Identifies an appropriate labeling of the faces, such as 1, 2, 3, 3, 4, 4.

Teacher Notes

Objectives A, B, I, L

Concepts and Skills This activity requires students to:
- read information from text, a table, and a picture.
- make decisions based on given data and real-life experiences.
- add fractions and mixed numbers.
- calculate absolute value.
- use the Putting-Together Model for Addition to form sentences involving addition.
- calculate magnitudes of turns.
- summarize results.

Materials
- rulers marked in customary units

Guiding Questions
- Why do you think the dashed-line path stops a few inches in front of the refrigerator?
- Why is the robot programmed to TURN 45 when it reaches the refrigerator?

Answers

a. Sample: TURN 45 MOVE $2\frac{1}{16}$
TURN -90 MOVE $3\frac{3}{4}$

TURN -90 MOVE $\frac{5}{8}$;
Sample: TURN 180 MOVE $\frac{5}{8}$
TURN 90 MOVE $3\frac{3}{4}$

TURN 90 MOVE $2\frac{1}{16}$ TURN 135

b. Sample: $12\frac{7}{8}$ yards

c. Answers will vary.

Extension
Have students identify paths between key points in the classroom, measure the distances, and create sets of commands to move the robot between the points.

Evaluation

Level	Standard to be achieved for performance at specified level
5	The student demonstrates an in-depth understanding of addition and measurement, and may ask several probing questions. All measurements and calculations are accurate and complete. The student may take the initiative to identify one or more alternative paths for any given location. The written report is neat, thorough, and easy to read, and it may be presented imaginatively.
4	The student demonstrates a clear understanding of addition and measurement. The student chooses several appropriate locations and paths for the robot, makes all necessary measurements, and performs all required calculations, but the work may contain minor errors. The written report is neat, thorough, and easy to read, but reflects the minor errors.
3	The student demonstrates a fundamental understanding of addition and measurement, but may need assistance in approaching the given situation. The student chooses several appropriate locations and paths for the robot, but there may be one or more major errors or omissions in the student's measurements and calculations. The report reflects these errors, and it may be somewhat disorganized and difficult to read.
2	The student demonstrates some understanding of addition and measurement. However, even with assistance, the student has a great deal of difficulty in choosing appropriate locations and paths for the robot. The student attempts to take measurements and calculate angles and distances, but there are significant errors or omissions. The student's report is jumbled and incomplete.
1	The student demonstrates little if any understanding of addition and measurement. Even when prompted, the student is unable to choose appropriate locations or paths for the robot. The student may take some measurements or perform some calculations, but they are superfluous or irrelevant. In preparing a written report, the student may simply copy or restate the given information.

1. When $a = 2$, $a^2 = 4$ and $2a = 4$. So, your friend says this is proof that a^2 has the same meaning as $2a$. Is your friend correct? Explain why or why not.

2. Make up a real-life problem that you could solve using this diagram. Then show how to use the diagram to solve your problem.

Objective G

☐ Is able to use special cases to determine that a property is false or to give evidence that it is true.

☐ Recognizes that the friend's conclusion is incorrect.

☐ Gives a logical explanation, such as showing that the expressions do *not* have the same value when $a = 1$ or $a = 3$.

Objectives I, K

☐ Demonstrates an ability to use a drawing to solve a real problem.

☐ Makes up an appropriate real-life problem, such as finding the number of games when five teams play each other once in a tournament.

☐ Shows a correct solution of the problem, such as 10 games.

3. Refer to the chart at the right. What do you think is meant by a *semiprime number*? Write a definition of the term. Use your definition to explain why 9 is *not* semiprime. Then name four semiprime numbers that are not listed.

The following are the first ten semiprime numbers.

6 (because $6 = 2 \times 3$)
10 (because $10 = 2 \times 5$)
14 (because $14 = 2 \times 7$)
15 (because $15 = 3 \times 5$)
21 (because $21 = 3 \times 7$)
22 (because $22 = 2 \times 11$)
26 (because $26 = 2 \times 13$)
33 (because $33 = 3 \times 11$)
34 (because $34 = 2 \times 17$)
35 (because $35 = 5 \times 7$)
38 (because $38 = 2 \times 19$)

Objectives C, D

☐ Understands the meanings of prime and composite.

☐ Is able to determine the meaning of unknown terms.

☐ Writes a reasonable definition of a semiprime number, such as *a number that can be expressed as the product of two different prime numbers.*

☐ Determines that 9 is not semiprime because 3×3 is not a product of *different* prime numbers.

☐ Names four other semiprimes, such as 39, 46, 51, and 55.

4. Refer to the advertisements at the right. Is it true that you pay more to park at Acme? Or is it true that Acme has the best rates in town? Explain how you could use a handwritten table or a spreadsheet to answer these questions. Which garage would you say has the best rates?

Midtown Garage	Acme Garage
$4.95 first hour $.60 each additional hour	$5.45 first hour $.45 each additional hour
Why pay more at Acme?	*We have the best rates in town.*

Objectives E, J

☐ Demonstrates an ability to use a handwritten table or a spreadsheet to answer questions in real situations.

☐ Gives a logical explanation of using a table or spreadsheet.

☐ Recognizes that Midtown's rates are better for 4 hours or fewer ($6.75 or less) than Acme's ($6.80 or less); and that Acme's rates are better for 5 hours or more ($7.25 or more) than Midtown's ($7.35 or more).

Teacher Notes

Objectives A, B, D, E, J

Concepts and Skills This activity requires students to:
- read and interpret data presented in a table.
- find the meaning of unknown words.
- explore the meaning of negative differences.
- find patterns and make generalizations.
- create a spreadsheet.
- use a spreadsheet to answer questions in real situations.

Materials
- spreadsheet software, if available

Guiding Questions
- If you do not understand some of the abbreviations, where do you think you could find an explanation?
- Why do you think some of the entries in the *Change* column are negative numbers?
- If you do not understand the term "density," how can you find its meaning?

Answers
a. Answers will vary.
b. The 1970 population was subtracted from the 1990 population.
c. and d. Check students' spreadsheets and formulas. Formulas for Part d involve dividing population figures by land area.
e. Answers will vary, but might include finding the increases (decreases) in population density from 1970 to 1990.

Extension
Have students research population data for the states in your region for each decade from 1900 through 1990. Have them create a spreadsheet to display the data and calculate the change in the total population of the region from decade to decade. Have students create a graph to illustrate the change from decade to decade, and then describe any trends they observe.

Evaluation

Level	Standard to be achieved for performance at specified level
5	The student demonstrates an in-depth understanding of the given situation, and may ask several probing and insightful questions. The spreadsheet is thorough, well-organized, and easy to read, and all calculations are accurate and complete. The student uses the data to generate several meaningful facts, and may even make an effort to generate analogous data for the other regions of the country.
4	The student's work demonstrates a clear understanding of the given situation and the mathematics involved. The student creates a spreadsheet that is well-organized and easy to read, and uses the data to generate at least three other meaningful facts. The student may make some minor errors in observing patterns or in devising appropriate formulas, and the spreadsheet reflects these errors.
3	The student demonstrates a fundamental understanding of the given situation and the mathematics involved, but may need some assistance in getting started. The student observes patterns in the data and attempts to devise appropriate formulas, but may make one or more major errors. The spreadsheet reflects these errors, and it may be somewhat disorganized.
2	The student demonstrates some understanding of the given situation and the mathematics involved. However, the student is able only to observe patterns in the data and devise formulas with a great deal of assistance, and even then makes major errors in calculation or omits critical steps of the process. The spreadsheet reflects the errors and omissions, and is very jumbled and difficult to read.
1	The student demonstrates little if any understanding of the given situation or of the mathematics involved. Even with prompting, the student is unable to observe patterns in the data, and there is no meaningful effort to devise formulas. The student may attempt some calculations, but they are superfluous or irrelevant. The student may create a spreadsheet by simply copying the given data.

1. Describe three real-world situations that you can represent by the subtraction -4 − 5. Find the difference.

Objectives A, K, L, M

☐ Understands the differences among models for subtraction.
☐ Describes an appropriate take-away situation, such as losing 5 points when already 4 points "in the hole."
☐ Describes an appropriate slide situation, such as a temperature of -4° dropping 5°.
☐ Describes an appropriate comparison situation, such as comparing temperatures of -4° and 5°.
☐ Can subtract the two numbers and gets result of -9.

2. Write two different equations that are equivalent to -2 − x = 9. Explain how you know the equations are equivalent.

Objectives B, G

☐ Demonstrates an ability to solve sentences of the form $x - a = b$ and $a - x = b$.
☐ Is able to apply the properties of subtraction.
☐ Understands equivalent equations.
☐ Writes two equivalent equations, such as $-x = 9 + 2, -2 = 9 + x$, or any equation whose solution is -11.
☐ Gives a logical explanation.

3. Every student in Paulo's class has a cat or dog as a pet. Paulo says 25 students have a dog and 14 have a cat. Rita says there must be 39 students in the class. Is she correct? Use a Venn diagram to explain your answer. What is the *least* number of students in the class?

Objectives N, P

☐ Understands the Putting-Together with Overlap Model for subtraction.
☐ Draws appropriate Venn diagrams to describe or determine overlap.
☐ Recognizes that some students may have both a cat and a dog, so Rita is not correct.
☐ Recognizes that there could be as few as 25 students in the class.

4. Quadrilateral *ABCD* is a parallelogram, with m∠*A* = 90° and *AB* = *CD*. What special type of parallelogram is *ABCD*? Be as specific as you can, and explain how you know.

Objectives F, I

☐ Is able to apply the definitions of special quadrilaterals to determine their properties.
☐ Can find measures of angles and sides in special quadrilaterals without measuring.
☐ Identifies quadrilateral *ABCD* as a rectangle.
☐ Gives a logical explanation.

5. Write ten facts about the relationships among the lines and angles that are labeled in the figure at the right.

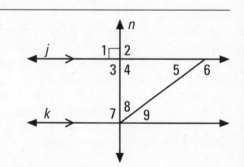

Objectives C, D, H

☐ Is able to find measures of angles in figures involving linear pairs, vertical angles, and perpendicular lines.
☐ Demonstrates an ability to find measures of angles in figures involving parallel lines and transversals.
☐ Writes ten valid facts, such as:
   $j \parallel k$; $n \perp j$; $n \perp k$;
   m∠1 = m∠2 = m∠3 = m∠4 = m∠7 = 90°;
   m∠5 + m∠6 = 180°; m∠4 + m∠5 + m∠8 = 180°;
   m∠8 + m∠9 = 90°; m∠5 = m∠9

Teacher Notes

Objectives A, M

Concepts and Skills This activity requires students to:
- read data from text and from a table.
- make decisions based on given data and real-life experiences.
- round, compare, and compute with fractions, mixed numbers, and decimals.
- make a chart.
- summarize results.

Guiding Questions
- How many shares of a stock can you buy with $5,000 if one share costs exactly $50? $25? $20?
- What information would you want to know about a company before investing in it?

Answers
a. $+9\frac{3}{8}; -2\frac{1}{2}; -1\frac{1}{2}; +4\frac{3}{4}; -1\frac{3}{4}; +2\frac{3}{8}; +\frac{5}{8}; +8\frac{1}{4}$

b. Bin Co: 171; CDR: 198; DysH: 116; EngR: 259; GenCm: 129; KJCo: 370; MasWy: 111; NSys: 277; PCGen: 161; TynD: 117; VNG: 320; YszCo: 173

c. Estimates may vary. Check students' work.

d. and e. Answers will vary.

Extension
Have students use newspaper reports to follow the progress of one or more stocks for one week. Have them determine how much they would have gained or lost on a $5,000 investment in each stock over the course of the week.

Evaluation

Level	Standard to be achieved for performance at specified level
5	The student demonstrates an in-depth understanding of the situation and of the mathematics involved. The chart is well-organized and easy to interpret, and it may be rendered imaginatively. All calculations are accurate and complete. The student presents a sound plan for further investment and provides an articulate explanation. The student may offer additional insights into the situation.
4	The student demonstrates a clear understanding of the situation and of the mathematics involved. The chart is well-organized and easy to read, but it may lack in some detail. The student may make minor errors in computation or estimation, and these errors are reflected in the chart. The student effectively outlines a plan for further investment.
3	The student demonstrates a fundamental understanding of the situation and of the mathematics involved, but may need some assistance in getting started. The student prepares an appropriate chart, but it may reflect one or more major errors or omissions in the student's computations or estimates. The student prepares a plan for further investment and provides a satisfactory rationale.
2	The student demonstrates some understanding of the situation and of the mathematics involved, but needs considerable assistance in performing the given tasks. There are several major errors or omissions in the student's computations and estimates. The student prepares a chart, but it is disorganized and incomplete. There is a plan for further investment, but no satisfactory rationale.
1	The student demonstrates little if any understanding of the situation and of the mathematics involved. Any attempts at calculation or estimation are superfluous or irrelevant. The student prepares a chart by simply copying the given data. There is no meaningful effort to prepare a plan for further investment.

EVALUATION GUIDES

1. Create a set of twelve numbers that satisfy the following conditions.

   The range is 41.
   The median is 25.
   The mode is 11.

   Make a stem-and-leaf display of your data.

Objectives A, I

☐ Is able to find the median, range, and mode of a set of numbers.
☐ Creates an appropriate set of numbers, such as 3, 7, 11, 11, 11, 25, 25, 29, 30, 41, 42, 44.
☐ Makes a correct stem-and-leaf display such as that shown.

0	3 7
1	1 1 1
2	5 5 9
3	0
4	1 2 4

2. Mai Lin has collected data about the cost of a one-day video rental at ten different stores in her town. Why do you think it might help to display the costs in a graph? What type of graph do you think she should use? Explain your choice.

Objectives F, G, H

☐ Understands reasons for having graphs.
☐ Demonstrates an understanding of bar graphs and/or coordinate graphs.
☐ Gives an appropriate reason for using a graph, such as ease in comparing costs.
☐ Identifies an appropriate type of graph, such as a bar graph.
☐ Gives a logical explanation.

3. Write an equation for a line that contains the point (-1, 4). Explain how you know that your line contains that point.

Objectives J, K

☐ Draws and labels an appropriate coordinate system.
☐ Can plot and name points on a coordinate graph.
☐ Demonstrates an ability to graph equations of the form $x + y = k$ or $x - y = k$.
☐ Writes an appropriate equation, such as $x + y = 3$ or $x - y = -5$.
☐ Gives an appropriate explanation.
☐ Draws a correct graph of the line.

4. Complete the figure below so that line m is a line of symmetry. Then draw *all* lines of symmetry of your completed figure.

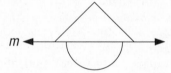

Objectives B, C

☐ Is able to draw the reflection image of a figure over a line.
☐ Can identify the symmetry lines of the figure.
☐ Completes the figure correctly, as shown at the right.
☐ Draws four lines of symmetry in the completed figure.

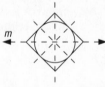

5. Suppose your friend is having difficulty understanding the difference between a *translation image* and a *reflection image* and has asked for your help. Use the figure at the right to write an explanation for your friend.

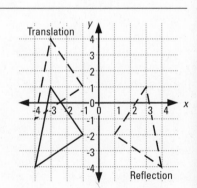

Objective L

☐ Is able to interpret reflections and translations on a coordinate graph.
☐ Gives an appropriate explanation of a translation image. See example at the right.
☐ Gives an appropriate explanation of a reflection image. See example at the right.

Teacher Notes

Objectives C, D, E

Concepts and Skills This activity requires students to:

- use data from text and pictures.
- make decisions based on given data and real-life experiences.
- identify the symmetry lines of a figure.
- identify translations.
- apply the relationships between figures and their reflection and translation images.
- extend the fundamental region of a tessellation to cover a given area.
- find a percent of a number.
- estimate and calculate measurements and costs.
- summarize results.

Materials

- rulers, graph paper

Guiding Questions

- How will you represent one brick on the graph paper? How will you represent the floor?
- Is there more than one way to estimate the number of bricks needed?

Answers

a. Jack-on-Jack (2 lines), Ladder Weave (1 line), Basket Weave Variation (2 lines)
b. Herringbone
c. Whorling Square. Not all shapes in the pattern are congruent.
d. Answers will vary.
e. Answers will vary, but should be near 160.
f. Answers will vary, but should be near $100.

Extension

Some paving bricks are made in the shape shown at the right. Have students determine how the shape was created. Then have them use the basic 4-inch-by-8-inch rectangular shape to create their own original designs for paving bricks.

Evaluation

Level	Standard to be achieved for performance at specified level
5	The student demonstrates an in-depth understanding of transformations and tessellations and may offer additional insights or ask probing questions. All calculations are accurate and complete, and estimates are reasonable. The student's drawing is neat, thorough, and accurate, and it may be rendered imaginatively. The student may prepare two or more alternative patterns.
4	The student demonstrates a clear understanding of transformations and tessellations. The student plans an attractive pattern for the floor and prepares a drawing that is neat and easy to read, though it may lack in some detail. The student may make some minor errors in calculation or estimation, and these are reflected in the drawing.
3	The student demonstrates a fundamental understanding of transformations and tessellations. The student chooses a pattern and prepares a drawing that contains the essential elements of the pattern, but it may be somewhat disorganized and difficult to read. There may be one or more major errors or omissions in the student's calculations and estimates, and these are reflected in the drawing.
2	The student demonstrates some understanding of transformations and tessellations, but needs considerable help in applying the concepts to the given situation. There is an attempt to calculate the number of bricks and to estimate a cost, but the student makes one or more major errors or omissions in the process. The student's drawing is jumbled and incomplete.
1	The student demonstrates little if any understanding of transformations and tessellations. Even with prompting, the student is unable to choose a pattern or attempt the task of paving the floor. Any calculations or estimates are superfluous or irrelevant. The student may prepare a drawing by simply copying the given figures at random.

1. Use the figure at the right to show a multiplication of two fractions. What multiplication did you show? What is the product?

Objectives C, M
☐ Is able to picture multiplication of fractions using area.
☐ Demonstrates an ability to multiply fractions.
☐ Illustrates and states an appropriate multiplication such as $\frac{3}{4} \times \frac{1}{3}$.
☐ Gives the correct product as $\frac{1}{4}$.

2. Suppose that the product rst is negative. What can you say about the numbers represented by r, s, and t? Explain your reasoning.

Objectives D, E, F
☐ Can multiply positive and negative numbers.
☐ Is able to identify and use properties of multiplication.
☐ Recognizes that exactly one or exactly three of the numbers r, s, and t must be negative.
☐ Gives a logical explanation.

3. Give an example of two independent events A and B that satisfy these conditions.

   $Prob\,(A) = 40\%$ $Prob\,(B) = 40\%$

   What is $Prob\,(A$ and $B)$?

Objective I
☐ Can calculate probabilities of independent events.
☐ Identifies two appropriate events, such as a basketball team winning a game today and winning a game tomorrow.
☐ Identifies $Prob\,(A$ and $B)$ as 16%, or $\frac{4}{25}$.

4. Explain the relationship between these two conversion factors. Then give an example of the use of each.

   $$\frac{2.54 \text{ centimeters}}{1 \text{ inch}} \quad \text{and} \quad \frac{1 \text{ inch}}{2.54 \text{ centimeters}}$$

Objectives J, K
☐ Can apply the Rate Factor Model for Multiplication.
☐ Is able to use conversion factors to convert from one unit to another with examples such as 4 in. = 4 • 2.54, or 10.16, cm; and 12 cm = 12 • $\frac{1}{2.54}$, or about 4.7, in.
☐ Recognizes that the first factor is used to convert inches to centimeters, and the second is used to convert centimeters to inches.

5. Examine the rectangular solid below. Draw a rectangular solid of equal volume, with a different height. Be sure to label all the dimensions on your drawing.

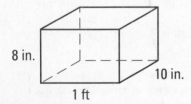

8 in.
10 in.
1 ft

Objectives B, H
☐ Can find the volume of a rectangular solid.
☐ Recognizes that the volume of the given solid is 960 in.³
☐ Sketches a box of appropriate dimensions, such as 6 in. by 10 in. by 16 in.

6. On a coordinate grid, you draw a triangle and its image under a size change of magnitude -0.5. Tell as many things as you can about the relationship between the image and the preimage.

Objective N
☐ Can do size changes on a coordinate graph.
☐ Makes several valid observations about the relationship, such as:
   They have the same shape.
   Corresponding image and preimage sides are parallel.
   Lengths of sides of the image are half the lengths of corresponding sides of the preimage.
   The image is rotated 180° from the preimage.

Teacher Notes

Objectives A, B, C, G, H, J, K, L, N

Concepts and Skills This activity requires students to:
- use data from text, a picture, and a table.
- make decisions based on given data and real-life experiences.
- explore scale drawings.
- find the areas of rectangles and right triangles.
- find the volume of rectangular solids.
- explore volumes of nonrectangular solids.
- multiply fractions.
- apply the Rate Factor Model for Multiplication.
- apply the Size Change Model for Multiplication.
- perform an expansion on a coordinate grid.

Materials
- graph paper

Guiding Questions
- If you could move the rose bed and the open section together, what shape would result?
- How can you calculate the area of the rose bed?
- How can you calculate the volume of gravel needed for the open section?

Answers
a. Sample answers are given.
  hostas: $l = 6$ ft, $w = 5$ ft;
  begonias: $l = 10$ ft, $w = 5$ ft;
  petunias: $l = 8$ ft, $w = 6$ ft;
  roses: $l = 12$ ft, $w = 10$ ft
b.–d. Answers are based on responses given for Part a.
b. 94 ft^3
c. $13\frac{2}{3}$ ft^3
d. about 50 begonias, 7–8 hostas, 24 petunias, 30 rose bushes

Extension
Have students research the cost of peat moss, gravel, and plants at one or more local garden supply centers and calculate the cost of the materials for the garden.

Evaluation

Level	Standard to be achieved for performance at specified level
5	The student demonstrates an in-depth understanding of multiplication and measurement concepts. The student makes intelligent choices for dimensions of the flower beds, and easily devises methods for finding volumes associated with the triangular beds and the paths. All calculations are accurate and complete. The drawing is neat and accurate, and it may be rendered imaginatively.
4	The student demonstrates a clear understanding of multiplication and measurement concepts. The student makes reasonable choices for dimensions of the flower beds, and is able to devise methods for finding volumes associated with the triangular beds and the paths. The student performs all necessary calculations, but may make minor errors. The drawing is neat, accurate, and easy to read.
3	The student demonstrates a fundamental understanding of multiplication and measurement concepts, but may need some assistance in getting started or in devising appropriate methods for finding volumes associated with the triangular beds and the paths. The student may make one or more major errors in computation, or may omit a major step of the process in determining the needed amounts of materials. The drawing is essentially complete, but may be disorganized and difficult to read.
2	The student demonstrates some understanding of multiplication and measurement concepts, but needs considerable assistance in applying them to the given situation. There is an attempt to assign dimensions to the flower beds and to determine the amounts of materials needed, but the student's work is disorganized and incomplete. The student's drawing is jumbled and inaccurate.
1	The student demonstrates little if any understanding of multiplication and measurement concepts. Even with prompting, there is no meaningful attempt to assign dimensions to the flower beds or to determine the amounts of materials needed. The student may perform some calculations, but they are superfluous or irrelevant. The student simply copies the given figure with no regard to scale.

1. Which of the following equations have the same solution as $-8t = 2$? Tell how you know.

   $-8t = -2$ $-2t = 8$
   $8t = -2$ $-4t = 1$

Objective A

☐ Can solve and check equations of the form $ax = b$.
☐ Recognizes that $8t = -2$ and $-4t = 1$ have the same solution as $-8t = 2$ $(t = -\frac{1}{4})$.
☐ Gives a logical explanation.

2. Make up a real-life problem that you can solve with this equation:

   $$5n + 128 = 340.50$$

   Use the equation to solve your problem.

Objectives B, G

☐ Is able to solve and check equations of the form $ax + b = c$.
☐ Can find unknowns in real situations involving multiplication.
☐ Makes up an appropriate problem such as: A plumber's total bill of $340.50 showed $128 for parts and a charge for 5 hours of labor. What is the charge per hour?
☐ Shows a correct solution of the problem, $42.50 per hour.

3. Make a drawing that shows how areas of rectangles illustrate the Distributive Property.

Objectives F, K

☐ Can represent the Distributive Property.
☐ Makes an appropriate drawing such as the following:

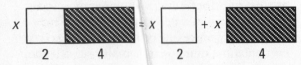

4. Alana simplified the expression $8k - k$ and said that the answer is 8. Explain why her answer is incorrect.

Objective C

☐ Can apply properties of multiplication to simplify expressions.
☐ Recognizes that $8k - k$ is equivalent to $8k - 1k = 7k$.
☐ Gives a logical explanation.

5. The rectangular solid shown below is a small box. Suppose its length, width, and height are each doubled. Would you need twice as much cardboard to construct the new box? Explain your reasoning.

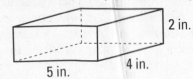

Objectives H, I

☐ Can find the surface area of a rectangular solid in a real context.
☐ Recognizes that the problem involves units of area.
☐ Recognizes that four times as much cardboard, 304 square inches (ignoring overlap), would be needed.
☐ Gives a logical explanation.

6. On the grid below, sketch a trapezoid whose area is between 40 and 50 square units. Show how to find the area of your trapezoid.

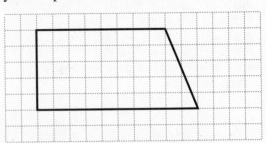

Objective E

☐ Can find the area of a trapezoid.
☐ Draws a trapezoid of the appropriate dimensions, such as $h = 5$, $b_1 = 8$, and $b_2 = 10$; $A = 45$ square units.
☐ Gives the correct method for finding the area of the trapezoid.

Teacher Notes

Objectives G, H, I

Concepts and Skills This activity requires students to:
- use information from text and a figure.
- make decisions based on given information and real-life experiences.
- find unknowns in real situations involving multiplication.
- find the volume and surface area of rectangular solids in a real context.
- pick appropriate units in measurement situations.

Materials
- rulers

Guiding Questions
- How do you know if the dimensions that you chose are reasonable or unreasonable?
- To determine the amount of cardboard, do you need to find a length, an area, or a volume?

Answers
a. 6; rectangular solid
b. a little less than 96 in.^{3}
c. Answers will vary. Possible response: $l = 6$ in., $w = 2$ in., $h = 8$ in.
d. Answers will vary. Check students' drawings.
e. Answers will vary. For the box described in Part c, with flaps that are $\frac{1}{2}$ in. wide, the amount needed is 173 in.^{2}
f. Answers will vary. For the box described in Part b, four nets can be cut from one sheet, and 172 in.^{2} would be wasted.

Extension
Have students plan nets for 12-oz and 24-oz boxes of the snack mix. Then have them draw all three nets to actual size, and cut and fold them to make the boxes.

Evaluation

Level	Standard to be achieved for performance at specified level
5	The student demonstrates an in-depth understanding of the situation and the mathematics involved, and may ask probing questions or offer significant insights. The student chooses reasonable dimensions for the box, and may suggest one or more alternatives. All computations are accurate and complete. The drawing is neat, accurate, and easy to read, and it may be rendered imaginatively.
4	The student demonstrates a clear understanding of the situation and the mathematics involved. The student chooses reasonable dimensions for the box, but may make one or more minor errors in calculating the required areas. The student's drawing is neat, accurate, and easy to read, but it reflects the minor computational errors, and it may lack in some detail.
3	The student demonstrates a fundamental understanding of the situation and the mathematics involved, but may need some assistance in visualizing the relationship between the solid and its net. The student chooses appropriate dimensions for the box, but may make one or more major errors or omit a major step in computing the required areas. The drawing contains all the essential elements of the net, but the labeling is inaccurate or incomplete.
2	The student demonstrates some understanding of the situation and the mathematics involved, but needs considerable assistance in choosing appropriate dimensions for the box and in visualizing the relationship between the solid and its net. There is an attempt to calculate the required areas, but the work contains several significant errors or omissions. The drawing is jumbled and incomplete.
1	The student demonstrates little if any understanding of the situation and the mathematics involved. Even with assistance, the student is unable to choose reasonable dimensions for the box or to visualize the relationship between the solid and its net. Any calculations that the student attempts are superfluous or irrelevant. The student produces a drawing that is fragmented or inappropriate.

1. The segment below is $5\frac{1}{2}$ units long. To need to divide it into 3 parts of equal length, what division should you do? Show how to find the quotient on the diagram.

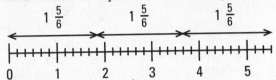

Find the quotient using the algebraic definition of division.

2. Describe two situations that can be represented by this division.

$$5 \div 7$$

One situation should involve rates, and the other should involve ratios.

Objective A

☐ Can divide fractions.
☐ Shows an appropriate division and quotient. ($5\frac{1}{2} \div 1\frac{5}{6} = 3$ or $5\frac{1}{2} \div 3 = 1\frac{5}{6}$).
☐ Shows how to find the quotient algebraically, using a reciprocal: $5\frac{1}{2} \div 3 = 5\frac{1}{2} \times \frac{1}{3} = 1\frac{5}{6}$

Objectives G, H

☐ Demonstrates an understanding of the differences between models for division.
☐ Gives an appropriate Rate Model situation, such as finding a unit price if 7 items cost $5.
☐ Gives an appropriate Ratio Comparison situation, such as finding what percent of the days of the week are school days.

3. The mean of a set of five temperatures is negative. Must all the temperatures in the set be negative? Give an example to support your answer.

4. Tom earns $25 for working 4 hours. To find the amount he would earn in working 18 hours, he wrote this proportion.

$$\frac{25}{4} = \frac{18}{n}$$

Explain why Tom's proportion is incorrect. Then write a correct proportion and use it to solve the problem.

Objectives B, E, F

☐ Can divide positive and negative numbers.
☐ Can apply the general properties for adding and dividing positive and negative numbers.
☐ Uses integer division in real situations.
☐ Recognizes that not all the temperatures must be negative.
☐ Gives an appropriate set of temperatures, such as -6, -4, -2, 0, and 2 (mean = -2).

Objectives C, I

☐ Can solve proportions.
☐ Is able to use proportions in real situations.
☐ Gives a logical explanation of the reason the proportion is incorrect.
☐ Gives a correct proportion, such as $\frac{25}{4} = \frac{n}{18}$.
☐ Identifies $112.50 as the solution.

5. Copy rectangle *ABCD* onto a sheet of graph paper. Then draw a rectangle *WXYZ* that is similar to *ABCD*. Explain why the rectangles are similar.

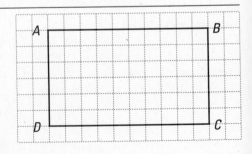

Objective J

☐ Can find lengths in similar figures.
☐ Draws a rectangle *WXYZ* of appropriate dimensions, such as 3 units by 5 units, 9 units by 15 units, or 12 units by 20 units.
☐ Gives a logical explanation of the reason the rectangles are similar, such as: Lengths of pairs of corresponding sides have the same ratio, 1 to 2, 3 to 2, or 2 to 1.

Teacher Notes

Objectives F, G, H, I

Concepts and Skills This activity requires students to:
- use information from text.
- make decisions based on given information and real-life experiences.
- use integer division in real situations.
- use the Rate Model for Division.
- use the Ratio Comparison Model for Division.
- solve proportions in real situations.
- make a graph.

Guiding Questions
- If you know the amount you earn in one week, how can you find the amount you earn in one year?
- Does the job that pays the most per hour also pay the most per year?
- In choosing a job, what factors should you consider besides the amount you earn per hour or per year?

Answers
a. about 30 hours
b. Reader for Blind Student ($5.60/hour)
c.–e. Answers will vary.

Extension
Provide students with the *Help Wanted* ads from one or more newspapers. Have them find five jobs that interest them and which have a salary or hourly wage given. Have them determine how long they would have to work at each job in order to earn $5000. Then have students research the types of deductions that typically are taken from an adult's paycheck.

Evaluation

Level	Standard to be achieved for performance at specified level
5	The student demonstrates an in-depth understanding of division, ratios, proportions, and percent. All calculations are accurate and complete. The student's choice of jobs, budget categories, and type of graph reflects careful consideration of several factors, and the student may offer additional insights into the given situation. The written budget and graph are accurate and easy to interpret, and they may be rendered imaginatively.
4	The student demonstrates a clear understanding of division, ratios, proportions, and percent. The student makes a reasonable choice of jobs and budget categories and chooses a sensible type of graph. The student performs all necessary calculations, but may make one or more minor errors. The written budget and graph are well-organized and easy to read, but may lack in some detail.
3	The student demonstrates a fundamental understanding of division, ratios, proportions, and percent. The student makes a reasonable choice of jobs, but may need some assistance in selecting budget categories and a type of graph. There may be one or more major errors or omissions in the student's work. The written budget and graph are essentially complete, but may be somewhat disorganized.
2	The student demonstrates some understanding of division, ratios, proportions, and percent, but needs assistance in applying the concepts to the given situation. The student makes reasonable choices of jobs, budget categories, and a type of graph, but may make several major errors in calculations or omit one or more major steps. The written budget and graph are jumbled and incomplete.
1	The student demonstrates little if any understanding of division, ratios, proportions, and percent. Even when prompted, the student makes no meaningful effort to address the given situation. Instead of preparing a written budget or a graph, the student simply copies the given information. The student may attempt some calculations, but they are superfluous or irrelevant.

1. How do you know that $\sqrt{55}$ is close to 7.4?

Objective B

☐ Can apply the definition of square root.
☐ Recognizes that the square root of 55 is between 7 and 8.
☐ Gives a logical explanation.

2. Use three of the lengths 40 mm, 42 mm, 50 mm, and 58 mm to draw a right triangle. Then use three of the lengths to draw a triangle that is *not* a right triangle. Describe the relationship that exists between the sides of the right triangle you drew.

Objective B

☐ Uses trial and error to draw a right triangle with lengths 40 mm, 42 mm, and 58 mm.
☐ Draws a non-right triangle.
☐ Demonstrates an understanding of the Pythagorean Theorem.
☐ Describes the relationship $a^2 + b^2 = c^2$ for the right triangle: $40^2 + 42^2 = 58^2$ (3364).

3. Danny used this method to find a simple fraction equal to $0.4\overline{09}$.

$$x = 0.4\overline{09}$$
$$10x = 4.\overline{09}$$
$$10x - x = 4.\overline{09} - 0.4\overline{09}$$
$$9x = 4 - 0.04 = 3.6$$
$$x = \frac{3.6}{9} = \frac{36}{90} = \frac{2}{5}$$

Find the error(s) in Danny's method. Then show a correct way to find the fraction.

Objective A

☐ Can find a simple fraction equal to a repeating decimal.
☐ Recognizes at least one error, such as multiplying by 10 or subtracting incorrectly.
☐ Finds the correct fraction, $\frac{9}{22}$.

4. The figure at the right is a triangular prism. Find values of x and y so that the volume of the prism is between 80 ft³ and 100 ft³. Use your values for x and y and find the volume of the prism.

Objective E

☐ Is able to find the volume of a prism.
☐ Gives appropriate values for x and y, such as $x = 5$ and $y = 6$.
☐ Gives a correct volume of the prism. For the values given, the volume is 90 ft³.

5. A spherical water storage tank has a 10-meter radius. If you double the radius, would twice as much water *fill* the tank? Would twice as much paint be enough to cover it? Explain your reasoning.

Objectives F, I

☐ Can apply the formulas for the surface area and volume of a sphere in a real situation.
☐ Recognizes that the surface area and volume would be more than doubled.
☐ Gives a logical explanation. For example, shows that the surface area would be 4 times as great and the volume would be 8 times as great.

6. Give as much information as you can about the size of the can of corn and the can label shown at the right.

Objectives D, E, H, I

☐ Can find the area and circumference of a circle.
☐ Is able to find the volume and the surface area of a cylinder.
☐ Gives several facts, such as: $d = 8.4$ cm, $r = 4.2$ cm, $h = 12$ cm for each base, $C \approx 26.4$ cm, $A \approx 55.4$ cm² for the label, $A \approx 316.8$ cm² for the can, $S.A. \approx 427.6$ cm², $V \approx 664.8$ cm³

Teacher Notes

Objectives C, H, I

Concepts and Skills This activity requires students to:
- use data from text and from a figure.
- make decisions based on given data and real-life experiences.
- use formulas for the area of a rectangle, for the circumference and area of a circle, and for the volume of prisms and cylinders.
- find the perimeter, area, and volume of a composite figure in a real situation.
- apply the Pythagorean Theorem.
- summarize results.

Guiding Questions
- What seems to be the relationship between AD and AB? between AD and WZ?
- What steps must you take to find the area of the track?

Answers
a. square, rectangles, and two half-circles (semicircles)
b. Answers will vary. Possible responses: **i., ii., iii.** 60 m.   **iv.** 20 m
c.-g. Answers will vary. Responses that follow are based on the dimensions suggested in Part b.
c., d. outer edge: about 308 m; inner edge: about 183 m
e. **i., ii.** about 85 m   **iii., iv.** about 63 m
f. about 4913.2 m^2
g. about 491 m^3

Extension
Have students make an enlarged scale drawing of the track on graph paper. Have them divide the track into four lanes and draw a finish line that crosses all four lanes. Then have them work backward to establish the starting line in each lane for a 200-meter race.

Evaluation

Level	Standard to be achieved for performance at specified level
5	The student demonstrates an in-depth understanding of real numbers and their application to measurement situations. The student chooses reasonable dimensions for the track, and may offer additional insights. All calculations are accurate and complete. The student summarizes the results in a manner that is well-organized and easy to read, and may develop a creative presentation.
4	The student demonstrates a clear understanding of real numbers and their application to measurement situations. The student chooses reasonable dimensions for the track and performs all the steps necessary to obtain the required measurements, but may make some minor errors in calculation. The student summarizes the results effectively, but the report may lack in some detail.
3	The student demonstrates a fundamental understanding of real numbers and measurement, but may need assistance in applying the concepts to the given situation. The student chooses reasonable dimensions, but may make one or more major errors or omissions in obtaining the required measurements. The student's report reflects the errors, and it may be somewhat disorganized.
2	The student demonstrates some understanding of real numbers and measurement, but can only apply the concepts to the given situation with a considerable amount of assistance. The student attempts to obtain the required measurements, but makes several major errors or omits one or more major steps of the process. The report reflects the errors, and it is jumbled and difficult to read.
1	The student demonstrates little if any understanding of real numbers and measurement. Even with prompting, the student is unable to choose reasonable dimensions for the track. The student simply copies the given figure, and there is no meaningful effort to obtain the required measurements. Any calculations that are attempted are superfluous or irrelevant.

1. Arrange these equations in a more sensible order. Tell how you chose the order. What is the solution of each of the equations?

   a. $5 = -3 - 16x$
   b. $8 = -16x$
   c. $5 + 9x - 9x = -3 - 7x - 9x$
   d. $5 + 9x = -3 - 7x$
   e. $3 + 5 = 3 + -3 - 16x$

Objective A

- [ ] Identifies a more sensible order, such as **d, c, a, e, b.**
- [ ] Explains that the order defines the steps in solving the equation $5 + 9x = -3 - 7x$.
- [ ] Can solve equations of the form $ax + b = cx + d$.
- [ ] Identifies -0.5 as the solution.

2. Graph each equation.

   a. $y = x$ b. $y = \lfloor x \rfloor$
   c. $y = \lceil x \rceil$ d. $y = x^2$

   Describe the shape of each graph.

Objectives F, H

- [ ] Can graph equations of the form $y = ax + b$.
- [ ] Is able to graph equations involving the symbols $\lceil \ \rceil$ and $\lfloor \ \rfloor$.
- [ ] Demonstrates an ability to graph parabolas.
- [ ] Gives an appropriate description of each graph: **a.** line; **b.** and **c.** collection of segments; **d.** parabola.

---

3. Which of these points does *not* lie on the same line as all the others?

   (6, -4)   (9, -6)   (-9, 6)   (4, -6)   (12, -8)

   Tell how you know. Then give an equation for the line on which the other points lie.

Objective C

- [ ] Can find the line on which the numerators and denominators of equal fractions lie.
- [ ] Recognizes that (4, -6) does not lie on the same line as all the other points.
- [ ] Gives a logical explanation.
- [ ] Gives a correct equation, such as $y = -\frac{2}{3}x$.

4. **a.** Find a value of x such that $\lceil x \rceil$ does not equal $\lfloor x \rfloor$.
   b. Are there any values of x for which $\lceil x \rceil$ equals $\lfloor x \rfloor$?

   Explain your reasoning.

Objective B

- [ ] Is able to evaluate expressions using the symbols for rounding up or rounding down.
- [ ] Gives values for x that are *not* integral for Part a and values for x that are integral for Part b.
- [ ] Gives a logical explanation.

---

5. The graph at the right shows the costs of canoe rentals at two shops. Describe the cost at each shop in your own words. What information do you get from the point (3, 6)? How could you get the same information without the graph?

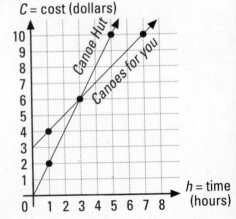

Objectives D, G

- [ ] Recognizes that the cost of *Canoes for You* is $3 plus $1 per hour of use, while the cost at *Canoe Hut* is just $2 per hour of use.
- [ ] Recognizes that (3, 6) indicates that the rental costs would be the same at both shops for a 3-hour rental ($6).
- [ ] Can translate a situation of constant increase into a sentence of the form $y = ax + b$ by fusing the equations $y = x + 3$ and $y = 2x$ to describe the two rates.
- [ ] Recognizes that the point at which the costs are equal can be found by solving $x + 3 = 2x$.

Teacher Notes

Objectives B, H

Concepts and Skills This activity requires students to:
- use information from text, a table, and a map.
- make decisions based on given information and real-life experiences.
- read and interpret the scale of a map.
- create and evaluate expressions using the symbols ⌈ ⌉ and ⌊ ⌋.
- graph equations involving the symbols ⌈ ⌉ and ⌊ ⌋.
- summarize results in a table and in a graph.

Materials
- compasses

Guiding Questions
- How will you choose an appropriate zone for a state when your compass mark passes through the middle of the state?
- What factors do you think you should consider in deciding on your rates?

Answers
a.–d. Answers will vary. Check student's work.

Extension
Have students research the methods used by several different mail-order companies in determining their shipping and handling charges (total amount of order, total weight of order, distance from distribution center, and so on). For each company, have students make a graph of the charges, if possible, and then determine if an equation can be used to describe the graph.

Evaluation

Level	Standard to be achieved for performance at specified level.
5	The student demonstrates an in-depth understanding of coordinate graphs and equations and their application to real-life situations. The student makes sound decisions concerning delivery zones and rates, and may ask probing questions. All calculations are accurate and complete. The table and graph are neat, accurate, and easy to interpret, and they may be rendered imaginatively.
4	The student demonstrates a clear understanding of coordinate graphs and equations, and readily applies the concepts to the given situation. The student makes appropriate decisions concerning delivery zones and rates. The student performs all necessary calculations, but may make one or more minor errors. The table and graph are neat and easy to interpret, but may lack in some detail.
3	The student demonstrates a fundamental understanding of coordinate graphs and equations, but may need some help in applying the concepts to the given situation and in determining delivery zones and rates. The student may make one or more major errors or omit a significant step in following through on the decisions. The table and graph may be somewhat disorganized and difficult to read.
2	The student demonstrates some understanding of coordinate graphs and equations, but can only apply the concepts to the given situation with a considerable amount of assistance. The student attempts to determine delivery zones and establish rates, but there are several major errors or omissions in the work. The student prepares a table and a graph, but they are jumbled and incomplete.
1	The student demonstrates little if any understanding of coordinate graphs and equations. Even with prompting, the student is unable to apply the concepts to the given situation. There is no meaningful effort to establish delivery zones or rates. The student may attempt some calculations, but they are superfluous or irrelevant. Rather than preparing a table or graph, the student simply copies the given information.